VIRAGO

Noel Streatfeild was born in Sussex in 1895 and was one of three sisters. After working in munitions factories and canteens for the armed forces when the First World War broke out, Noel followed her dream of being on stage and went to RADA where she became a professional actress.

Streatfeild began writing children's books in 1931 and *Ballet Shoes* was published in 1936. She quickly became one of the most popular authors of her day. She was one of the first winners of the Carnegie Medal and was awarded an OBE in 1983.

D0865622

Also available in Virago Children's Classics

BY JOAN AIKEN

The Gift-Giving

The Kingdom and
the Cave

The Serial Garden

BY NINA BAWDEN

Carrie's War

Keeping Henry

The Peppermint Pig

BY SUSAN COOLIDGE

What Katy Did

What Katy Did
at School

What Katy Did Next

BY L. M. MONTGOMERY

Anne of Green Gables

Emily of New Moon

Jane of Lantern Hill

BY EDITH NESBIT

Five Children and It

The Phoenix and the Carpet

The Story of the Amulet

The Treasure Seekers

The Wouldbegoods

New Treasure Seekers

The Railway Children

BY RUMER GODDEN

An Episode of Sparrows

Dark Horse

Listen to the Nightingale

Thursday's Children

BY NOEL STREATFEILD

Apple Bough

Caldicott Place

BY P. L. TRAVERS

I Go By Sea, I Go By Land

The Fox and the Manger

NOEL STREATFEILD

author of *Ballet Shoes*

Apple Bough

virago

VIRAGO

This paperback edition published in 2018 by Virago Press

First published in Great Britain in 1962 by William Collins Sons & Co. Ltd

1 3 5 7 9 10 8 6 4 2

A CIP catalogue record for this book
is available from the British Library.

ISBN 978-0-349-01091-5

Typeset in Goudy by M Rules

Printed and bound in Great Britain by Clays Ltd, Elcograf S.p.A.

Papers used by Virago are from well-managed forests
and other responsible sources.

MIX
Paper from
responsible sources
FSC
www.fsc.org   FSC® C104740

Virago Press
An imprint of
Little, Brown Book Group
Carmelite House
50 Victoria Embankment
London EC4Y 0DZ

An Hachette UK Company
www.hachette.co.uk

www.virago.co.uk

For My
AMERICAN GOD-DAUGHTER
Priscilla McOstrich

WITH MUCH LOVE

Apple Bough Remembered

When anyone mentioned Apple Bough the four Forum children gave each other remembering looks. For Apple Bough had been their home in Essex.

In the children's memories it had been an absolutely perfect house. It had lots of large rooms – which the grown-ups remembered as shabby and difficult to keep clean – but the children remembered as beautiful, for in them everything was their own. Apple Bough was gloriously unchanging; you could, the children reminded each other, put down something that belonged to you and nobody moved it. These books and toys which nobody moved had grown fabulous in their minds because it was so long since they had seen them, for they together with the furniture, curtains and carpets, in fact almost everything except their clothes, had been put into store.

'And if there is one thing more annoying than another,' Myra, the eldest, would say, 'it is not being able to have your own things when you want them.'

'There is something nicer than anything else,' Sebastian, the next eldest, would add, 'about coming into a house where nothing is strange, where everything is exactly where you know it will be.'

Apple Bough had a garden which in the children's memories was the size of a public park. Nobody in the family was a gardener so the garden had run excitingly wild. Raspberries, strawberries, currants and gooseberries which nobody had planted would be discovered suddenly, buried under some other plant but with fruit growing on them. Plants that usually are considered wild came into the Apple Bough garden to flourish – cowslips on the lawn, primroses and a wild kind of daffodil in the weedy drive, dog roses grew where ordinary gardens had proper rose trees, and in the autumn the whole garden looked as if it was covered in snow, there was such a lot of travellers' joy climbing over everything.

Best of all at Apple Bough they had a dog. His name was Wag, a plain name. 'But then,' as Myra was quick to explain, 'we like plain names, I think it's because ours mostly aren't.'

Wag was Myra's dog for when he was a puppy a farmer had given him to her, but he was considered the family dog. He was mostly poodle but his paternal grandmother, it was believed, had been a dachshund, which explained his unusually short legs and the length of his body. But as he was never given a poodle-cut like town poodles, he did not look much like a poodle anyway, so the dachshund bits didn't stand out.

Leaving Wag behind when Apple Bough was sold was so terrible a thing that Myra still could not think about it without getting a lump in her throat. It was true he went away with Miss Popple's brother, of whom he was fond, but Myra knew he knew he was being left, for his poor tail was down and there was no heart behind the last lick he gave her. Myra was, her mother said, 'born sensible' so she made no outward fuss about leaving Wag, for she was told the life they were to lead was not suitable for him, he would be happier with Mr Popple. But secretly she would pretend in hotels, apartment houses, on boats, trains or aeroplanes that he was sitting on her knee or lying on her bed, and then she knew with every bit of her it was not true. 'You're happier here with me, aren't you, Wag? You don't mind all this travelling as long as I'm here, do you?'

On journeys the children played a game they called 'remembering'. Though they had left Apple Bough when Myra was nine, Sebastian eight, Wolfgang seven and Ethel five, sometimes they remembered so well they could see what they were remembering. It was on a flight from New York to San Francisco when they were playing 'remembering' that Myra had said:

'I remember a brick which was loose in the kitchen floor.'

It was like a door opening in their minds. Wolfgang, whose seat was really across the gangway but who was half leaning, half sitting on Sebastian, said:

'It lifted up. I put that silver button I found under it.'

Sebastian could see the brick.

'That's where I put my ring out of the plum pudding.'

Ethel, who was sitting between Sebastian and Myra, bounced up and down. She spoke fast to prevent anyone arguing.

'My sixpence! I had a sixpence with a hole in it, that's there.'

Myra and Sebastian exchanged looks. Nobody wanted to discourage Ethel from having a share in Apple Bough, but that did not stop them knowing she often made up what she could not remember.

'I don't think you ever had a sixpence with a hole in it, Ettie,' Sebastian said. 'But we'll count it as remembering, I mean you needn't lose a life.'

Myra looked out of the window at the clouds lying below them like a huge field of fat sheep. How marvellous, she thought, if someone would pass a law that every child had to have a home, and it would be extra nice if that home had to include a kitchen with a loose brick in the floor. Bringing up a child like Ettie, without any home at all, was a great responsibility for you had to let her get away with such a lot of things just to make up. She turned back to the family.

'I put my magic bean under it.'

It was in a way Sebastian's fault that Apple Bough had been sold, for it was because of him they were always travelling. Back in the days when the family had lived in Apple Bough, David, the children's father, had been the only one who went away. He was a pianist, not the sort who plays solos but the sort who accompanies soloists. David was always busy for he was considered one of the best accompanists in the country. Luckily much of his work was in London so he could spend quite a lot of time at Apple Bough. He would come home very late after concerts, driving himself in the family's disreputable old Ford car, and Myra and Sebastian could remember hearing their mother run to the door to call out, 'How did it go, darling?' They could remember too knowing how glad their mother was that their father was home safely, for he was the vaguest man, particularly after concerts, so he was quite likely to go to the wrong house, or even the wrong village. In fact, until they had the Ford car, when he had come home by train, he was always being carried past their station. Perhaps because the concerts were more personal their father had become vaguer since they started their world tours.

One parent being vague would be enough in most families, but the Forum children had two. Their mother, Polly, had been training to be a professional singer when she met and married David. After she married she gave up training but music was still in her so she was inclined to get what she called 'carried away' when she heard anything played especially beautifully. Though most people would have thought that looking after a house and four children was enough for anybody it was not what Polly wanted, so after she stopped learning to sing she taught herself to be an artist. At first she only meant to be an artist for fun, but soon painting got such a hold of her that she became an artist first and a housewife second. If artists as a class could get prizes for vagueness Polly would have won a first.

Both David and Polly came from musical families. David's father was a parson-choirmaster. His church was always packed for, apart from his own parishioners, people came from miles around to hear his choir sing. His mother was the church organist and a very good one. Polly's father was what people call 'something in the City' by profession, but his heart was given to his hobby – chamber music. Her mother had been, when she was young, the star of her local operatic society and was still, when the children were born, what she described as 'warbling a bit'. So, with all this music about, it was naturally supposed the babies would grow up to be musical, perhaps, taking after their father, they would be pianists. It was with this idea firmly fixed that their names were chosen. Myra because of Dame Myra Hess. Sebastian because of Hans Sebastian Bach. Wolfgang because of Wolfgang Amadeus Mozart. Ethel because of Dame Ethel Smyth. Of course nobody called Wolfgang by his name, he was either Wolfie or just plain Wolf. Ethel too had her name shortened, for it seemed such a grand sort of name for the baby of the family, so she became Ettie.

Before each baby could walk, let alone talk, David and Polly experimented, looking for signs of appreciation of music. David would play the piano while Polly studied the babies' reactions. Also, suitable gramophone records were put on, so was an old musical box which played 'The last rose of summer' with perfect pitch. Perhaps because they had music in their blood each baby in turn had reacted in an exciting way. Myra, who had listened spellbound to any music almost from birth, would burst into tears as soon as the piano lid was closed or the record or musical box turned off. Sebastian, before he was old enough to be experimented on, lying face downwards on Polly's knee having his nappy changed, had tried to conduct an orchestra who were playing Beethoven on the wireless. Wolfgang who, even when a baby, was a natural show-off, while left in his pram outside the village store startled passers-by by humming (it was long before he could talk) 'The last rose of summer' in (so it was said) perfect tune. Ethel had danced in time to any tune before she could walk properly.

But these early signs of promise had borne no fruit except in Sebastian. Not that the other three were not musical children; they were. But, as each in turn had piano lessons, though all three learned to play quite nicely, soon David was writing to his parents, and Polly to hers, to say that Myra or Wolfgang or Ethel were born amateurs. Actually Wolfgang had musical talent of a sort, for from the age of four he was composing sloppy little tunes, which made his parents shudder so they were never spoken of.

It had taken longer than it should have to discover Sebastian's talent. This was because both David and Polly took it for granted the piano must be his instrument. But though, for a small boy, he played remarkably well, there seemed to be something missing. Then, when he was four, he and Myra were taken to their first concert. At first the music had been too much for Sebastian, so he had curled up into a ball trying to shut a little of it out, but David and Polly had expected that.

'It'll be easier soon,' David whispered, 'when the piano plays alone.'

But it was not the piano playing alone that made the music easier for Sebastian but a solo passage for the fiddles, for then he knew it was their calling and answering voices which had almost hurt they were so lovely. So he uncurled and smiled blissfully, like a kitten who has drunk a large bowl of milk. It was then that Polly and David exchanged a look over his head. The sort of look fathers and mothers always give each other when they learn something new and

7

interesting about one of their children. That look said as clearly as anything, 'We must buy him a fiddle.'

For the next three years life went on much as usual at Apple Bough except that Sebastian was taken each week to London for violin lessons, and he practised daily, starting with one hour but soon working three and sometimes four hours a day. Not because anyone made him but because he liked doing it. His father had bought him a little fiddle; it was quite a nice instrument and certainly the best they could afford, but it did not, to Sebastian's acute ear, sing as the violins had sung at that first concert. He never said anything about this to his father and mother for they would worry, but he explained it to Myra.

'There's a thing violinists do called vibrate. I can't do it for I don't understand how they do it. But I think when I can do it my violin will sing properly. That's what I'm practising so hard for.'

Sebastian was learning from a young player called Peter Pond. A good violinist but not a born teacher. In their childish way the children understood this.

'Can't he show you how?' Myra asked.

Sebastian put an imaginary violin under his chin and turned, so Myra could watch his fingers.

'It's a sort of shake. I know how it looks but my fingers are stupid.'

'Don't fuss,' Myra said. 'I expect one day it will just happen.'

And one day it did just happen, and from that moment Sebastian learnt so fast he startled Peter Pond and charmed himself.

8

'My fiddle sings now,' he told Myra. 'It's got a beautiful little voice.'

Because of Sebastian's violin lessons he could not go to an ordinary school, and so it was decided a governess should be engaged who could teach all the children.

'For it wouldn't be good for Sebastian to have lessons alone,' Polly told David. 'Because we hope he'll grow up to be a professional musician it's most important he shouldn't feel different from other children.'

So Miss Popple came into the family, and from the day she arrived it felt as if she must always have been there. She was what Myra called apple-ish-looking. This meant she had reddish-coloured hair, shining red cheeks and a generally rounded look. Though she came as a governess, and was a governess for she taught lessons to all the children, she was much more. She was by nature what Polly was not – she was a manager. So quite soon, as well as teaching lessons, she was cleaning, mending and, best of all, cooking meals. For Miss Popple, or Popps as the children were soon calling her, was a beautiful cook. Right in the middle of long division, without looking at a clock, she knew to a second when a pie should come out of the oven or the joint be basted. She thought nothing of making a batch of scones or a cake while giving a history lesson. In fact, lessons were often taught in the kitchen, and even when they were in the room used as a schoolroom Miss Popple mostly darned or mended while she taught.

Every family has to have one person who is dependable. Almost as soon as she came into the house Miss Popple knew that person must be Myra. Although she herself arrived at nine in the morning and did not leave until after tea, there was still a lot left of the day which needed looking after. And there were also Saturday afternoons and all Sundays when she was at home in the cottage she shared with her brother. So, though Myra was only six when they first met, the others were even smaller, and therefore more in need of looking after.

Miss Popple, long before she came to the house, knew just how vague and unlike most people's mothers Polly was, for it was something much talked about in the village. Indeed it was a miracle, the village women said, that the Forum children looked so well and so happy, for what they got to eat and when they got it was anybody's guess with their mother painting away in her studio with no more idea of time than a starling.

All the same, they could not help liking Polly, and though they clicked their tongues when they heard she had rushed into the village shop at one o'clock with paint on her nose, overall and trousers and said: 'What shall I buy? There's nothing for lunch,' they tried when they could to be helpful, though the thought of a baby like Ettie living on nothing but tinned food made them shudder. They groaned even more about David for nobody could say he looked well. Actually, David was well but he was the thin kind and the life he led was not the sort to put weight on a person. That was in the days before the Ford car so most mornings he had to rush through the village soon after eight to catch a train, and lots of heads were shaken as he ran. 'No breakfast in him like as not, and only a sandwich for his dinner, shouldn't wonder. He ought to have a good hot supper when he gets home, but I doubt she'll remember to cook it.'

Myra, when Miss Popple first saw her, was a funny-looking child. All the Forums were small, and in height Myra might have looked much less than her six years, but if you looked at her face she could have been ten. All the family were dark, and Myra had a lot of dark straight hair held out of the way with a piece of pinkish tape which had once tied a bundle of music together. Clothes, before Miss Popple came, were chancy in the Forum family, so she was not surprised on a cold February day to find Myra wearing cotton jeans. It is true that over these was pulled a heavy grubby jersey but there were such large holes in the jersey that Miss Popple was afraid it must let in a lot of cold air. But it was the face looking up into hers that held her attention. Myra had such huge dark eyes which at that moment were looking very worried.

'Mummy said Sebastian and I would do our lessons in the back room, but I can't make the fire stop alight. Mummy lit it, Sebastian's still blowing it. And I don't know what we're to do with Wolf and Ettie – Mummy said they could be with us but they aren't really big enough for lessons and mostly they are noisy – you know how they are at that age.'

Miss Popple held out a hand.

'I'm sure we'll manage. Where is your mother?'

'Painting, she said only to interrupt if it was something desperate. She's having a show and she's got to get a picture finished.'

Hand in hand Miss Popple and Myra went to what was to be called the schoolroom. Sebastian was lying on his face before a very black fire trying by mouth to coax a tiny flame into becoming a blaze. The room was icy.

'How do you do, Sebastian?' Miss Popple said. 'Don't bother with that. We'll do our lessons in the kitchen this morning. Kitchens are usually cosy.'

Sebastian rolled over and stood up. He too was small for his age and he too had dark hair which, Miss Popple noticed, badly needed a cut for it hung in his eyes and had to be repeatedly brushed back. He was more warmly dressed than Myra, Miss Popple was glad to see, in a flannel shirt and corduroy slacks. He was a nice-looking little boy though, she suspected, far less on the spot than Myra, in fact he was probably as vague as his parents. He had good manners though. He held out his right hand.

'How do you do? I don't think our kitchen is cosy.'

'It isn't,' Myra agreed, 'but I have washed up breakfast so it's clean.'

Miss Popple was not worried.

'It will be cosy. You show me where it is and by the time I've lit the stove and seen to whatever there is for lunch it will warm up beautifully.'

On the way to the kitchen they collected Wolfgang and Ethel, who were playing being horses in the kitchen passage. Wolfgang was at that time only just four but even at that age he was a show-off. He stopped being a horse the moment he saw Miss Popple and gave a beautiful bow.

'Miss Popple I per-soom.'

Wolfgang was the best-looking of the family. There was red in his dark hair and it curled. Unlike the others his eyes were dark blue, not brown. They were shown off by enormously long eyelashes. He was amusingly self-possessed and wore his short red pants and very torn check shirt with an air.

'You presume right,' said Miss Popple. 'How old are you?'

'Four. Wouldn't you think I could do lessons?'

Miss Popple could see it would be far less nerve-racking to have the children working where she could see them than playing around where she could not.

'You could and so can this little person.' She looked at Ethel. 'You must be Ettie.'

In spite of being dressed in ill-fitting tartan slacks and a jersey too large for her Miss Popple could see that, though not so handsome as her brothers, Ettie was beautifully made. Evidently none of the Forum children were shy for Ettie made quite a long speech. But though voluble she was not distinct, and Wolfgang translated for her.

'She says she likes you and she'll like doing lessons.'

But Ettie was not putting up with that insult.

'I are talkin' like any lady,' she said clearly and snubbingly.

'Of course you are,' Miss Popple agreed. Then, because they had reached the kitchen where there was no sign of preparations for lunch, she added: 'Today, just to get used to each other, there won't be lessons, instead you'll all help me cook.'

2

The Letter

Though Myra never knew it, Miss Popple was the person who arranged she should be given Wag. It happened because Miss Popple's brother, who was a vet, said one morning at breakfast:

'That poodle, Sally, at Pond Farm had a litter of puppies a week or so back. Funny how that dachshund strain persists, each of the puppies has a trace of it.'

As if it was something she had been planning for days a fully made idea hopped into Miss Popple's head.

'Oh, Dan, do you think old Bush would give one of his puppies away?'

Her brother was amused.

'I should have thought you'd enough on your plate with the four Forum kids without adding a puppy.'

'It's not for me. It's for Myra. She's such a funny solemn little thing, she never plays about like the younger two. I think she would if she had a puppy.'

'What about Sebastian, does he play about?'

Miss Popple was not just not musical, she was anti-music

and could not understand why other people liked listening to it.

'Him! Poor child, every free moment he's up in his bedroom scraping away on that violin. It must be bad for him, but when I tell his mother so she just laughs and says 'Try and stop him.' Thank goodness there is a stove in his bedroom which is kept going, because apparently you can't play a violin with cold hands.'

Dan had finished his breakfast so he got up.

'I'm passing Pond Farm so I'll ask about a puppy.'

'If he says yes tell him I'll send Myra up with a message so he can give the present himself, I don't want the child to know I had anything to do with it, for the puppy will seem more her own coming from outside.'

Every afternoon when it was fine enough Miss Popple took Myra and Wolfgang for a walk. Ethel she pushed in her push-chair. Sebastian never came for he practised all the afternoon. On one of these walks Miss Popple stopped by the sign which said 'To Pond Farm.'

'Myra, run up to the farm and ask Mrs Bush for twelve eggs, brown if possible.'

'I'll go too,' said Wolfgang. 'I like Mrs Bush and Mrs Bush likes me.'

It was now March so Miss Popple was used to Wolfgang.

'I expect Mrs Bush likes Myra too.'

Wolfgang looked proud.

'Not as much. She said I was a most 'riginal child.'

Myra looked sorrowfully at Wolfgang.

'He's terrible, Miss Popple, but it's perfectly true, it's what she did say, I heard her.'

Miss Popple spoke in her firmest voice.

'She's not going to get a chance to say anything like that today. Run along, Myra.'

The children knew by now that when Miss Popple spoke in that voice she had to be obeyed. So Myra climbed over the stile and ran up the footpath to the farm. Wolfgang, who could not be crushed, looking after her, said, as if to himself: 'Actually, Wolfie wasn't wanting to see Mrs Bush.'

About ten minutes later, with her enormous eyes shining as Miss Popple had never seen them shine, Myra was back holding Wag in her arms.

'He's mine! Mr Bush gave him to me, he said I was not to worrit, you'd be mortal pleased for me to have a dog.'

Wag, though he was tiny and had for the first time left his mother, was wonderfully composed. He let first Wolfgang and then Ethel hold him, though that included a lot of kisses on his little soft head, and he was not then used to being kissed.

'This is all-of-ours puppy,' said Wolfgang. 'You can see he thinks he belongs to me as well as you, Myra.'

Again Miss Popple used her strict voice.

'Myra will let you play with the puppy, I am sure. But he belongs to her, puppies need one owner who looks after them and feeds them. What will you call him, Myra?'

'Something grand,' said Wolfgang.

'How about Orlando like the story book?' Miss Popple suggested.

Wolfgang was shocked.

'You can't call a dog because of a cat.'

Miss Popple looked at Myra.

'It's for you to decide.'

At that moment Myra took back the puppy from Ethel, and, as if he knew in whose arms he belonged, he wagged his little tail.

'Wag,' said Myra. 'It's what he does and it's a dear plain little name in a house where most of the names are grand.'

Wag did make Myra play more and look less serious but at the same time, as she grew older, she became more and more the dependable type her family needed. It was she and Miss Popple who planned the meals, who, between them, did most of the housework, mending, laundry lists and all the other things that need seeing to in a house. And it was they who made the arrangements for getting Sebastian met in London on the days when neither parent could take him, and it was they who met his train on his return. Sometimes Miss Popple was fussed inside in case she was expecting too much of Myra, but a little thinking showed her that Myra would have even more cares on her small shoulders if she were not in charge, and that the child liked mothering her family, so she would be miserable if she were ordered instead to run away and play.

Polly, when first Miss Popple had arrived, had continued in her own sort of way to run her house, though from Miss Popple's first day she had stopped rushing out to buy tins of something. Wolfgang had been sent to the studio to fetch her.

'Lunch, Mummy. It's called Irish stew. Us all made it.'

Eating in pleased surprise the truly delicious stew, Polly said to Miss Popple:

'I must get something for the children's tea.'

Miss Popple shook her head.

'There's no need, dear. I've made a huge dripping cake. There was no dripping in the house so I fetched some when I went to the butcher for the meat. I also made a fish pie and some soup for yours and Mr Forum's suppers. I couldn't find any cereals so I brought a packet for the children's supper. I hope that was right.'

'Right!' sighed Polly joyously, finishing her plate of stew. 'Of course it's right. If you really don't mind I'll hand the housekeeping money over to you.'

'That will be splendid,' Miss Popple agreed. 'Myra and I will have fun planning menus, won't we, dear?'

Polly did go on struggling with the housework. She would get up early to rush round with a duster and sweeper and to lay and light the fires and, though it was never at the same time two days running, helped by Myra she got the breakfast. But quite soon Miss Popple managed to make a better arrangement.

'If you could light Sebastian's stove and lay the school-room fire there's no need for you to do anything else, except breakfast of course. For when I get to the house it's easy for the children and I to get through the housework. It's exercise for them and, if we do it all together, it's fun.'

Polly looked shamefaced.

'You really mean I do it so badly you'd rather do it yourself because then you'll know it's well done?'

Miss Popple had eyes that laughed, they laughed at that.

'You're not a born housekeeper, are you?'

'How true! The awful thing is I resent hanging around brushing and mopping when all of me is screaming to get to the studio. Besides, I'm so forgetful, half the time I can't remember what I've done and not done.'

'Then give up trying so hard,' said Miss Popple. 'I'll tell you before I leave each day what I haven't had time for.'

Because she had more time for painting and no interruptions, such as getting the lunch or running out to see that the children were all right, Polly got into the habit of finishing work at teatime. Almost every day she joined the children and Miss Popple at tea, and after Miss Popple had gone she played with the children until they went to bed. She was a wonderful inventor of games, so usually the house or garden between tea and bedtime rang with laughter and sometimes, when the games were too exciting, with screams. Then the people in the village would smile at each other. 'Doing nicely now at Apple Bough since vet's sister took over.'

Even David found things better since Miss Popple had come to the house. There was always something nice for his supper, and though he could not describe what was different he knew the house seemed pleasanter; things were never lost like they used to be, and he always had clean, mended clothes to put on.

Nobody could say that after Miss Popple came the children looked smart, but there were improvements. She got some money from Polly and took them by bus into Dunmow, their nearest town, and bought each a pair of warm trousers for cold days and a pair of jeans, and they each had one new jersey and one cotton shirt. The clothes they owned when she came to the house she mended or, if too far gone, she threw away. In fact, sometimes, on their afternoon walks, she let herself feel quite proud. 'They are clean,' she thought, 'no holes anywhere, and their hair shines. That's all you need in the country.'

Then one day in the spring, just before Myra's ninth birthday, when Sebastian was eight, Wolfgang six-and-a-half and Ethel, whose birthday was just after Myra's, rising five, the letter came which changed their lives. The family had just finished their breakfast when the postman arrived. It was supposed to be turns collecting the post, and it was Ethel's day, but Wolfgang, followed by Wag, got there first.

'Good morning,' he said grandly, elbowing Ethel back. 'A pleasant day for the time of year.'

The postman clicked friendly fingers at Wag.

'You're a caution, you are, Wolf, and you don't improve.' He knew the customs of the house so he looked round Wolfgang at Ethel. 'Your day, is it? Here you are, duckie, all typed but the one.'

The one untyped letter was for David. He looked at the clock to see if he had time to read it, then, deciding that he had, opened the envelope and glanced at the signature.

'It's from Peter Pond. What have you been up to, Sebastian?' He read the letter then he put it in his pocket and got up. He went round the table to kiss Polly. 'I'll talk to you about what's in this tonight. Come on, you four.'

Seeing David off was a regular thing, but now, instead of going with him to the gate as they used to do, the children and Wag went to the garage to pack him into the Ford. That morning, as soon as the car had gone, they clustered round Sebastian.

'Did you know he was going to write?' Myra asked
Wolfgang sounded hopeful.

'Did you do something bad?'

'Couldn't it be something nice like what would Myra and me want for our birthdays?' Ethel suggested.

Wolfgang looked at her with a snubbing expression.

'Mr Pond doesn't know you and Myra.'

But Ethel stuck to her point.

'He knows about us, Sebastian tells him.'

'Not really, Ettie,' Myra explained. 'When Sebastian's with him they only talk music. That's right, isn't it, Sebastian?'

Sebastian was looking hunched up and miserable.

'Don't say anything to Mummy or it might put her off that picture she's finishing, but I knew he was going to write some time. He says he hasn't any more he can teach me.'

Myra and Wolfgang understood at once how worrying this was.

'Does he know someone else to teach you?' Wolfgang asked.

Sebastian kicked at a stone.

'He says I'm ready for someone really good.'

Myra leant down to pat Wag.

'They'd be terribly expensive, wouldn't they?'

'Terribly,' Sebastian agreed. 'That's why I said don't say anything to Mummy because she'll fuss trying to see how to manage it.'

Other children might have told Sebastian he himself was not to fuss, that something was sure to be arranged, but not the Forums. They were brought up with music and knew good teaching was desperately important.

'Daddy might have an idea,' said Myra. 'Perhaps you aren't too young for a scholarship somewhere.'

As soon as Miss Popple arrived she knew something was worrying Myra and Sebastian. Wolfgang was not the worrying sort and Ethel had not really understood. Over the washing up she asked Myra what was wrong. Myra did not know how to explain about music lessons being important to a person with no music in them.

'It was a letter Daddy had. Sebastian's afraid it's about Mr Pond thinking he ought to have a new teacher.'

Miss Popple struggled to understand.

'Oh, poor Sebastian. I do sympathise. I hate changes too. Still, I expect he can still see Mr Pond even though he goes to somebody else for his classes.'

Myra realised that, to Miss Popple, all you had to do was to write or telephone a violin teacher and say Sebastian was coming for lessons. So she gave up trying to explain.

'It made Sebastian lowish, and we're not telling Mummy. Daddy's doing that tonight.'

To Miss Popple there was very little that could not be cured by hard work. So as soon as the washing up was done she called all four children into the hall.

'Spring cleaning begins today. It's a glorious morning. We'll start by taking the rugs and carpets out into the garden where we can give them a good beating.'

It was a lovely morning. The primroses were open, the wild daffodils in bud, there was a fuzz of green on the branches of the trees, the sky was pale blue, and every bird singing a Te Deum because the spring had come back. An hour's rolling out of carpets and beating the dust out of them and even Sebastian felt happy. It was silly to fuss, Daddy knew thousands of fiddle players, he was sure to find someone to teach him.

But Sebastian did not hear the talk David and Polly had after he was in bed. David had Peter Pond's letter.

'Listen to this :

"'I am afraid the time has come for me to hand young Sebastian on to someone else. I have taught him all I know, he's ripe now for a great master.

"'Would you and Polly allow Sebastian to play at the charity for the Musicians' Fund next month? He is ready, I think, and there should not be too much strain if you, as the committee hope, would be at the piano.'"

The concert seemed the least important part of the letter.

'A great master,' groaned Polly. 'That's all very fine but where's the money coming from for a great master?'

David lit his pipe because it helped him to think.

'That's only part of it. He's outgrowing that little fiddle. He must have a larger one and it should be good, and you know what that costs.'

Polly was frowning.

'What I can't make up my mind about is how much we ought to spend on Sebastian. Already he costs twice as much as the others, and they may want to train for something later on. I think Ettie ought to go to dancing classes in a year or two. She dances that Irish jig I taught them all like an angel.'

'It's a puzzle,' David agreed. 'Peter, as you know, thinks

Sebastian could be one of the great, and he may be right. He certainly is not a little boy when his fiddle is under his chin.'

'Well, he's just an ordinary little boy, thank goodness, except when he's playing, and that's how he's going to stay, bless him.' Then Polly remembered the last part of the letter. 'What about this concert? Why don't we see if something comes of that? All the top-notchers go to that concert, perhaps someone will offer Sebastian first-class lessons free.'

David laughed.

'Dear Polly! You are such an optimist, but I think the concert is a good idea. I'll ring in the morning and say Sebastian may play at it, and though I can't see anyone taking him on free it's quite possible someone will step forward with a bright idea as to who should take him on next.'

Polly yawned for it was getting late.

'I must try and remember to ask Miss Popple what Sebastian has got that's suitable to wear on the platform at a rather grand concert.'

'Do that,' David agreed. 'I don't fancy his appearing in a jersey and corduroy slacks, which is all he seems to own.'

'I'm tying a knot in my handkerchief.' Polly turned a worried face to David. 'I'd better get us both a glass of hot milk or we'll be going through the names of fiddle players all night.'

3

The Concert

The knot in the handkerchief worked. For the next morning Polly delayed going to her studio so that she could tell Miss Popple about the concert.

'We don't want a fuss made for his father thinks Sebastian should feel playing at a concert is no more frightening than playing to us on Sundays.'

Miss Popple thought that incredible.

'Does he indeed! Well, he ought to know I suppose, but I must say I should find it a terrifying experience.'

That made Polly laugh.

'I'm sorry to laugh but you must agree the thought of you playing a fiddle at a concert is funny.'

Miss Popple shuddered.

'Don't! I might dream it was happening, it would be as awful as my dream that I'm walking up the aisle in church wearing nothing but a vest, gloves and my Sunday hat.'

'Which reminds me,' said Polly, 'of what I came to talk

to you about. Clothes for Sebastian. His father thinks what he has won't do.'

Miss Popple was very fond of Polly but that did not blind her to her failings, one of which was the way she dressed her children.

'His father is quite right, nothing he has will do. And if you were thinking of taking Myra and Wolf to the concert they'll need new clothes too.'

Polly looked surprised.

'Will they? They always look all right to me. But I don't think I'll take the children. Sebastian and his father will work like mad at whatever they decide he's to play, so they'll be bored with hearing it. However lovely a piece of music is it's like over-eating if you hear it too often.'

'I'm sure of that,' Miss Popple agreed. 'Once is too much for me. Now clothes. What did Mr Forum say would be right?'

'He didn't, he just said he couldn't wear what he's got. I suppose the sort of thing pages wear at weddings.'

Sometimes there were concerts in the village hall which Miss Popple and Dan attended, and always children from the school performed.

'I think shorts and a shirt and tie are more usual.'

Polly made a face.

'How dull! But perhaps you can get shorts in a gay colour, crimson would look well with his dark hair.'

Sebastian was saved from crimson shorts by Dan who, hearing of the shopping expedition, said:

'Why do they want to poodle the poor kid up? Can't he play the violin without that?'

Miss Popple had a job to get Dan to do any dressing up so she understood his siding with Sebastian.

'All he's got is jeans and his corduroy slacks. Even you could not think either of those right on a platform. I am to buy him a shirt and shorts. Mrs Forum thought crimson shorts would be nice.'

Dan sounded as if he was going to be sick.

'Crimson! Give the kid a chance! He'll look like Little Lord Fauntleroy. Get him grey flannel and let him look like an ordinary boy.'

Miss Popple thought about Sebastian.

'But he's not ordinary.'

'All the more reason why he should look as though he was.'

Miss Popple thought that good sense.

'All right, grey flannel it shall be.'

While Miss Popple was deciding what Sebastian should wear, his father and Peter Pond were making up their minds about what he should play. When they had decided, just what Polly expected happened, David and Sebastian worked at the music together every spare minute until the rest of the family felt blown out with hearing it.

'It's not that I don't like the minuet,' Myra told Polly. 'It's beautiful, but before breakfast every day and most of Sundays spoils it.'

They were talking while they cleared the breakfast table. Wolfgang sprawled across it to reach the breadboard.

'It's much worstest for me. You don't share a bedroom with Sebastian like I do, so you don't have him singing the music all the time he dresses.'

'Never mind,' said Polly comfortingly. 'The concert will

soon be over and then Daddy and Sebastian will go back to their lovely Sunday music-making.'

Miss Popple had been afraid that Polly would go to the concert in trousers, for she had never seen her wearing anything else, but she was wrong. On the concert day Polly wore a dress, not Miss Popple's idea of a suitable dress for London for it was made of flame-coloured felt with fruit designed by herself appliquéd round the hemline, but still, a dress. Polly never wore a hat so instead she stuck a Spanish comb in her hair.

Miss Popple had to go to the concert. There was to be a party afterwards, which would bore Sebastian, so she was brought to take him home.

The other three children and Wag watched the car party set off. Sebastian very neat in grey flannel shorts, a white shirt and grey tie, clutching his fiddle case. Polly looking like a dragonfly. David in his afternoon concert suit. Miss Popple in her best coat and skirt and what she called her Sunday hat, which was blue with flowers on it.

The three children waved until the car was out of sight. Then they hung on the front gate. Wolfgang said:

'Poor Popps will have to take that Sunday hat off or nobody will see Sebastian because of her flowers.'

'Because of her flowers,' Ethel repeated.

Myra and Wolfgang pretended they hadn't heard that, for they were trying to cure Ethel of repeating things by ignoring her. Myra sounded worried.

'I feel awfully sorry for dear Popples. I can't imagine how it would feel not liking to hear music, but I suppose it's like not liking something to eat. Imagine spending all Saturday afternoon eating something you detested!' She climbed down off the gate. 'Oh, dear, I do feel wormish inside. How awful if Sebastian goes wrong.'

'Fuss, fuss, fuss,' groaned Wolfgang. 'Sebastian isn't caring at all so why should you?'

'Outside he isn't,' Myra agreed, 'but I bet he's squirming inside. I would be.'

'Oh, you! You'd be being sick by now. Come on, let's go and wake Dan up.'

It had been arranged by Miss Popple that while she was in London Dan should keep an eye on the other three. Keeping an eye meant to Dan putting a deck-chair in a sheltered corner and sleeping until it was time to meet the London train. In spite of Wolfgang's efforts he managed this.

'Come on, kids,' he said at about five o'clock, 'finish your tea, it's time we were off.'

'Good,' said Wolfgang. 'Now Wolfie can have some peace. Myra's fussed and fussed the whole afternoon.'

Sebastian, holding his fiddle case, followed by Miss Popple, came off the train looking, except for his clothes, exactly as he looked on an ordinary day when he came back from a violin lesson. He seemed surprised when the others and Wag rushed to meet him. Myra called out as she ran.

'How did it go? Were you all right?'

Sebastian always was vague after playing his fiddle, but he looked vaguer than usual.

'I think so. Daddy didn't say I wasn't.'

Wolfgang threw out his hands in a despairing way.

'You make everything so dull. Did they clap a lot?'

'Clap a lot,' Ethel echoed.

Myra saw they were not going to find out anything from Sebastian so she turned to Miss Popple.

'You tell us. Was Daddy pleased?'

Miss Popple's Sunday hat had slipped to one side, she looked flushed and bothered.

'I didn't have a chance to speak to him, dear. The room was crowded and your father and mother surrounded by people who were all talking at once. I thought Sebastian looked tired so we just slipped out.'

Dan joined them.

'Come on. You can talk in the car.'

'Yes, indeed,' Miss Popple agreed, 'for it's time I was putting Ethel to bed, and we must have supper early. Sebastian missed his tea.'

That brought Sebastian to life.

'We had superb buns at the station.'

In the car Myra made another effort to get Sebastian to talk. She had a frightened feeling that something was being hidden from them. How terrible if Sebastian had played badly. Daddy would mind awfully. Murdering music was the most shocking crime anyone could commit. But why should Sebastian have played badly, he never did? She hugged Wag to her for comfort.

'Did you play that encore?'

Sebastian nodded.

'Yes, the "Gipsy Airs." You knew I was going to play them.'

'Only if you were encored. You must have been all right if you got an encore, mustn't you?'

Sebastian tried to explain.

'It was queer, Myra. I thought it would be different at a

concert, but it isn't, it's just like playing at home. You don't hear anything but the music.'

Wolfgang bounced up and down in a fury.

'You make it all so dull. If it was me coming back from playing in a concert I'd talk and talk and tell and tell, nobody would make me stop.'

'Nobody would make me stop,' Ethel chirped.

Miss Popple was sitting in front beside Dan but she could hear what was said. She turned round to look at Wolfgang.

'Nobody doubts what you would be like after a concert, Wolfie. But what Sebastian needs now is food, not talk.'

'Something is wrong,' Myra whispered to Wag. 'I know it. I can feel it.'

Miss Popple was staying until David and Polly got home. Myra helped her put Ethel and Wolfgang to bed and to tuck up Sebastian. Then, unable to bear the suspense any more, she burst out:

'You're hiding something, aren't you, Popples? It ought not to be bad as there was an encore, but you look peculiar and Sebastian doesn't say anything.'

Miss Popple had brought down Myra's brush and comb meaning to do her hair. Now she sat down and let the brush and comb fall into her lap.

'You must never repeat this to Sebastian or your father and mother, but I missed hearing him play.'

'Missed hearing him!' Myra could not keep that she thought that appalling behaviour out of her voice. 'I know you don't like listening but it isn't a long piece, and it was his very first concert.'

'Don't be angry with me, dear. It was an accident. You see, the afternoon was warm . . .'

Myra was really shocked.

'You couldn't, you absolutely couldn't have gone to sleep?'

Miss Popple looked crushed.

'I did take a little nap, I'm afraid, in the first half, but Sebastian was playing in the second half, as you know. So in the interval I slipped out to get some air to blow the cobwebs away. I rested on a wall and I'm afraid I dropped right off again for the next thing I knew the concert was almost over.'

'But didn't you ask somebody how he was?'

Miss Popple looked like a dog who knows he is in disgrace but hopes forgiveness is in sight.

'I couldn't, dear, you must see that. It would have meant drawing attention to myself. Imagine if anyone knew Sebastian's governess was outside when he played, I mean, what would they think? No, I'm afraid I waited until the end and then I hurried round to the back.'

'Didn't Daddy or Mummy say anything? It isn't like them not to.'

'You can't picture it, dear. Everyone seemed excited and talking at once, it was not for me to push myself forward. I saw Sebastian sitting in a chair looking tired, I thought, so I found his coat, helped him into it, told someone to tell your mother we had gone and so we slipped out.'

Myra knelt down by Miss Popple's chair.

'You could see that no sister could go to bed not knowing. I shouldn't sleep all night.'

Miss Popple took up the brush and comb.

'Turn round so I can do your hair. I can understand that you are worried, so the moment they get home I will ask your father to run up to your room and, if you are awake, he can tell you what you want to know. I'm so ashamed to have failed you, dear, but even had I been in my seat I wouldn't have known how Sebastian played, for all music sounds alike to me, you know that.'

Polly and David came into the house soon after nine bursting with apologies.

'Oh, Miss Popple! Do forgive us,' said David. 'We meant to be back earlier.'

'You have had supper, haven't you?' Polly asked. 'You can imagine after all the excitement it was hard to get away.'

'Of course,' Miss Popple agreed, though wondering what the excitement had been about. 'I'll be off now. But, Mr Forum, would you go up and see Myra. She's anxious to hear how the concert went.'

David laughed.

'How like Sebastian not to have told her. I'll go up right away. Thank you for staying, bless you. Good night.'

But there was no need for David to go up for no sooner had Miss Popple left than Myra, her hair in two plaits and wearing her dressing-gown, came down the stairs.

'How did Sebastian play, Daddy?'

David sat down and pulled Myra on to his knee.

'How good do you think Sebastian is?'

Myra found it difficult to explain.

'When it's something he likes playing,' she said at last, 'I think he's nearly perfect.'

'Can a little boy of eight play the fiddle nearly perfectly?'

Myra clasped her hands as she felt for the right words.

'I don't think when he's playing he's the same Sebastian who does lessons with us and won't eat prunes.'

David looked at Polly. Then he kissed Myra.

'Important critics may agree with you. Sebastian was what they call a sensation this afternoon. Now you must run back to bed, darling.'

Polly went up with Myra to tuck her in. When she came down again she went to the window and stared out. The moon was up and in that light even their untidy garden took on a magic quality.

'What shall we do if one half of what they said to us today comes true? Ought we to allow him to play in public?'

David got up and joined her. He put an arm round her.

'It will need a lot of thought and nothing can be decided in a hurry. But one fact we have to face. It may well be that many things which I cannot afford to give him Sebastian can earn for himself. Including the best lessons money can buy.'

The next day all the papers wrote about Sebastian. Many of them said important things which, even when read out loud none of them properly understood. Sebastian did not even try to understand for since he came home from the concert he had been looking and feeling rather young for eight. But Wolfgang and Myra struggled.

'What's geni-us?' Wolfgang puzzled. 'A genie is that thing that came out of the magic lamp when it was rubbed.'

'I don't think it can mean that,' Myra said. 'For in the picture that's a sort of gold man not a bit like you, Sebastian.' She went back to her paper. '"Creative force is scarcely a term that can be used in referring to a small boy but when little Sebastian was playing he was not a child."'

Wolfgang picked up one leg and hopped round on the other singing to the tune of 'Yankee-doodle': 'Se-bastian is not a child. He's not a child when playing. He's just a genie from a lamp. And when he sings it sounds like neighing.'

Sebastian thought that funny but Myra did not.

'Shut up, Wolf, and listen, I can't read what it says when you make that noise, and we ought to know what the critics think, for Sebastian is our brother.'

4

Goodbye Apple Bough

The children knew something was going to happen for whenever their father was home he and their mother shut themselves into the studio and talked and talked. Just shutting doors was odd enough in Apple Bough, where all doors were kept open as it made it easier to shout to each other, but talking in low voices was odder still.

'It's as if it was before Christmas or a birthday,' Wolfgang said. 'That's the only time there's secrets.'

Then there were letters. Far more letters came than had come before, and when they arrived first David read them before throwing them to Polly to read, then they were put back in David's pocket while he gave Polly a 'We'll-talk-about-this-later' look.

Myra, lying in bed with Wag stretched out beside her, would hold one of his paws for comfort.

'Something I don't like is going to happen, Wag. I can feel it in my inside.'

No guess of the children's could have led them to what

their father and mother were discussing. An important American concert arranger called Paul G. Ruttenstein had been one of the audience at Sebastian's concert, and he had made an offer for Sebastian to tour America from what he called coast to coast. He was to give concerts accompanied by his father.

'Oh, no!' Polly had shuddered when she first read the letter. 'I won't have Sebastian turned into a horrid little prodigy.'

But David saw the other side of the picture.

'If his tour could finish in California, Misken lives in San Francisco. He's very choosy who he takes as pupils and he's known to hate infant prodigies, but it's worth a try. If Misken would take him on he could do wonders for Sebastian's fiddle playing.'

Polly understood that.

'I'm sure he would but Sebastian is only eight, too young to go off to America with only you to look after him.'

'I'll manage,' said David. 'If we decide it's the right thing.'

'How can you? He goes to bed early, you can't leave him alone in an hotel, you'll go mad child-sitting night after night. Anyway, it's not going to happen. We're a family and it's not right to break us up.'

'Not even if one of our children is said to be a bit of a genius?'

Polly knew her mind.

'No. We stay together.'

'Right,' said David. 'I'll write to Mr Ruttenstein today.'

The letter to Mr Ruttenstein was written, but that was not the end of the matter. Quite soon another letter arrived saying that Mr Ruttenstein quite understood how Mrs Forum felt and he thought she was quite right. Therefore he suggested a new contract, offering less payment for each concert but instead to pay the fares of the whole family so they could remain together.

'Now he's talking,' said Polly when she read this. 'It will be marvellous for the children. Imagine travelling all over America at their age!'

It was David who was doubtful that time.

'Ettie isn't five yet, don't you think that's rather young to tour America?'

By then Polly was miles away and breathless with excitement.

'Of course not. It'll be wonderful for her. She'll never need to learn her America from an atlas, she'll know it through her eyes. I wonder if I could have a picture show in San Francisco, perhaps Mr Ruttenstein could arrange it.'

David refused to let Polly make up her mind in a rush.

'This tour won't be the end of it, you know, more offers will come in. Can you really see yourself trailing round the world after Sebastian?'

'As long as we go as a family I don't care how much we travel. You write to Mr Ruttenstein and tell him so.'

After that David had several meetings in London with Mr Ruttenstein, for there was such a lot to decide. Then one evening he came with a big envelope under his arm. He handed it to Polly.

'There is Sebastian's contract signed and sealed. I only hope we haven't made a ghastly mistake.'

Polly waved the envelope as if it were a flag.

'It will be the most wonderful adventure. I can't wait to tell the children.'

David felt Polly might dash off there and then and wake the children up, so he laid a hand on her arm.

'Hold your horses. There's something else. I had lunch with your father in the City. He says we ought to sell this house.'

That was such a new idea Polly gasped.

'Sell Apple Bough. What's to happen to all our things?'

'Stored. Your father says this place is in poor repair and if we leave it for months it will get into so bad a state it will be past selling.'

Polly made a face.

'Oh, bother! All that packing up. Still, if Father says we ought to sell I expect he's right, he's very good about that sort of thing. Thank goodness for Miss Popple, I could never pack everything if she weren't here.'

'And that's another thing,' David said. 'Mr Ruttenstein suggests as soon as he is back in New York that he looks out for a good tutor for Sebastian who will be willing at the same time to teach Myra and Wolf.'

Polly stared at David, her eyes getting bigger and bigger.

'You never thought I'd go to America without Miss Popple, did you? I couldn't, I simply couldn't.'

David could feel he was in for trouble.

'That's a nice thing to tell me now the contract's signed. I don't suppose for a moment Miss Popple can get away. Who's to look after Dan?'

Polly refused to budge.

'If she can't come I'm not going. You can tear that silly

contract up. You and Sebastian can't go without me, I won't go without the rest of the family, and none of us can go without Miss Popple, so you can tell Mr Ruttenstein that's that.'

David saw it was no good reminding Polly that a contract was not something you could tear up without getting into trouble, and that she had agreed it was to be signed, for she never listened to reason when she was upset. So instead he said:

'You'd better talk to Miss Popple tomorrow. The sooner we know how we stand the better.'

Polly saw the sense of that.

'I shall tell everybody tomorrow, if Miss Popple needs persuading the children will help – they'll make her see that they can't go without her. She must see it would be cruel to allow them to miss such a marvellous opportunity of seeing the world.'

David had a nasty feeling that Miss Popple would say 'no'. She wasn't the sort to want to see the world. She probably liked her own cottage and living with her brother Dan. If she said no he could see himself having a very unpleasant talk with Mr Ruttenstein who, though he had been charming up to now, was not likely to agree to having his contract torn up. But he kept these thoughts to himself, only saying:

'You do that. It's time the children knew what's in the wind.'

The next morning, the housework done, cold lamb, potatoes in their jackets, a salad followed by a coffee junket planned for lunch, Miss Popple was just settling the children down to their lessons when Polly came in. It was so

43

unusual for her to leave her studio in the morning that they all, except Ethel, guessed that at last they were to be told the secret.

'Goody,' said Wolfgang, speaking for them all. 'You're going to tell us what you and Daddy have been mutter-muttering about.'

Polly sat down.

'I am, and very exciting it is. Daddy has signed a contract for you, Sebastian, to give concerts all across America, and as you and Daddy can't go alone we're all coming with you.'

The news was so startling that for a moment no one spoke. Then Sebastian asked:

'Is Daddy playing at the concerts with me?'

'Of course, darling, and he hopes you can finish your tour in San Francisco, where he's going to try to persuade Misken to give you lessons.'

David often talked to Sebastian about musicians, so he knew the magic name Misken. Now he whispered it as if it were a charm.

'Misken! Misken!'

Wolfgang got up and strutted round the table.

'This is Wolfie seeing New York.'

Ethel slid off her chair and followed Wolfgang.

'Ettie seeing it too.'

Myra felt as if all the breath had been knocked out of her. Going to America! Wag couldn't go to America, for if he did he would be in quarantine for six months when they came home. She licked her lips because they felt too dry to make words properly.

'When – when are we going?'

Polly turned to Miss Popple.

'All this depends on you, Miss Popple. If you can't go with us there will be no America for any of us.'

Three pairs of eyes were turned to Miss Popple. Myra's hopefully; surely dear Popps didn't want to go to America. Sebastian's anxiously; if there was a chance of his having lessons from Misken he must go to America. Wolfgang's dancing with excitement for any change suited him. Ethel had not understood so she continued to strut round the table.

Miss Popple was so surprised by what Polly had said that she had no breath for a moment to answer. Then at last she gasped:

'America!' Then, as thoughts tumbled round in her head, words just fell out of her mouth. 'America! Imagine me in America! Why, just going to London is an adventure. Oh, my goodness! What a thing to spring on me! I don't know what Dan will say. I mean he can't manage on his own.'

It was then the children interrupted, even Myra, though it was against herself to talk. For they knew almost everything that went on in the village.

'If you go to America,' said Myra, repeating what she had heard, 'Mary Bush up at Pond Farm will marry Dan.'

'Done it long ago if he weren't so comfortable along of his sister,' Wolfgang added.

Even Sebastian, far less up in local gossip, contributed his bit.

'If Dan Popple says snip that Mary Bush will say snap.'

Miss Popple knew the children were right. She turned to Polly.

'I'll have a talk with Dan tonight, Mrs Forum. If he agrees I believe – oh, dear, I'm too excited to think clearly, but I do truly think my answer will be "yes".'

The answer was 'yes'. So soon there was a board outside Apple Bough saying it was for sale and people arrived in cars to look at the house. Although Sebastian and Wolfgang were excited about America, even they did not like looking at the board, for nobody likes reading that their home is for sale. As for Myra, she never looked at the board for she always shut her eyes when she passed it. Then one day the board came down for Apple Bough was sold. That day Myra went to that bit of the garden where cow parsley grew nearly as tall as she was and she lay down under it and cried and cried.

After that life was all boxes and packing except for a gay day at the end of August when Dan married Mary Bush. Myra was one of the bridesmaids, wearing pink organdie made by Miss Popple, and Ethel and Wolfgang carried the train, Ethel in white and Wolfgang wearing a borrowed kilt in which he showed off dreadfully. Dan and Mary went for a week's honeymoon, then they came back to the cottage, so Miss Popple, all packed for America, moved into Apple Bough. The night Dan and Mary came back was the night Myra said goodbye to Wag, for the next day she and the other children were to be sent to stay with Grandfather and Grandmother in their rectory in Devonshire. They were to stay there until they were taken to Southampton to catch their ship.

Dan was a sensible man so he knew a lot of talking was a mistake when someone was saying goodbye to their dog, but he did promise Myra to write her regular news of Wag and he made it clear he knew he was only to be his dog temporarily, for his last words were:

'It's only six months, Myra, and I promise you wherever you stay when you come back I'll bring Wag to you first thing.'

But it was not six months, it was four years before the Forums lived in England again.

5

Rebellion

Sebastian became famous, so the first American tour was followed after a few months of lessons from the great Misken by another American tour. Then there was a tour of South America. Later that next year the whole family crossed the Atlantic again for a tour of Europe, but not of England for in England a child needs a licence to perform in public for money, and such a licence is never granted until a child is twelve. After the European tour there was a winter in Paris with lessons for Sebastian from a master Misken considered after himself the greatest in the world, a Russian called Dermidoff. By then Sebastian was not playing accompanied only by his father but with world-famous orchestras. Another series of American concerts and they were back in San Francisco, joyfully greeted by Misken. Then, after a few months' rest, off again to Australia, South Africa and Japan.

All the travelling was exciting at first and for David and Polly it remained exciting to the end. But by the second year Myra, Wolfgang, Ethel and Miss Popple longed for the months called by Mr Ruttenstein 'Rest Periods' when they stayed in one place. There, whether it was San Francisco, Paris, Melbourne or some other city, they could what Miss Popple called 'establish a routine'. The odd thing was that the farther they all travelled the more even Wolfgang loved routine.

'The nicest thing I know,' he said once, 'is eating tea at the same time at the same table knowing it'll go on being at the same time at the same table for weeks and weeks.'

Miss Popple was wonderful at making the apartments, flats, houses or rooms which were rented for Rest Periods into something which, if you had never known a real one, smelt faintly like a home. The first thing she did was to fix up a schoolroom and always, even in the most unlikely places, she made it look as much like the schoolroom at Apple Bough as possible. As Sebastian became more famous the Forums became richer until money ceased to be a worry, so during Rest Periods other teachers beside Miss Popple were hired: tutors who taught Latin and mathematics, French mistresses, and also the children went to outside classes. Sebastian, as well as daily fiddle lessons, went to schools of music to learn theory. Myra, Wolfgang and Ethel learnt gym, and Myra and Ethel were sent to dancing classes. And as well, Myra, Wolfgang and Ethel had daily piano lessons from their father, so whatever else they were Rest Periods weren't rests at all.

It is surprising how much thinking can go on inside people which, until something forces it out, stays inside. So, though by the second year Myra, Wolfgang, Ethel and Miss Popple were imagining how wonderful it would be to stay for ever in one place, none of them said so, which meant David and Polly never knew what they felt. For them life was perfect. Wherever they went they met musicians and spent hours talking music. For Polly each country she visited was exciting to paint, and often when they had a Rest Period she held a picture exhibition and, though she never became famous as Sebastian was famous, she was considered good and so made a large number of artist friends.

What Polly had been afraid of – that Sebastian would become a swelled-headed little prodigy – never began to happen. Sebastian on the platform was an artist; anyone could see by his inward-listening expression he was full of nothing but music, but in the artists' room he became a shy boy who loathed being made a fuss of. He was helped by the other three, who were generally taken to his concerts and usually rescued him. They would dash round to the artists' entrance and, while Wolfgang created a diversion by shaking any hand he could get hold of, Myra and Ethel would smuggle Sebastian out, just saying to the nearest grown-up, 'Tell our parents the children have gone.'

Polly and David said and believed that all the travelling they did was making the children world citizens. Actually, the more they travelled the more stubbornly English all four children became. It is true the girls curtsied when introduced to strangers, they all did more hand-shaking than is usual in England and they acquired a large variety of local catch-phrases, but otherwise they might have spent their time living in Apple Bough. They were noticeably British too about food. Every country has its special dishes and David and Polly, in all Rest Periods, hired a local cook. But if that cook tried to serve local dishes he or she was put off by Miss Popple, who would say:

'Not today. What I think we'll have is roast beef and Yorkshire. I'll show you how to cook it.' Or 'Just the weather for an Irish stew, with spotted dog to follow.'

Polly, when not painting, had moments when she bought clothes for the children which did for a time give them a world-citizen look. But the children (except Wolfgang) hated looking conspicuous and you do look conspicuous if you wear a large Japanese hat in Copenhagen, or leather *hosen* and a hat with a feather at the back in Chicago so, since much of their time was spent flying, Miss Popple was able to say: 'I'm afraid these things, charming as they are, must be left behind, we'll have no room for them on the plane.'

As had happened at Apple Bough ordinary clothes were chosen by Miss Popple. For this she had women's magazines sent out from England and from photographs and illustrations turned out the children looking as much like Prince Charles and Princess Anne as the local shops of whatever country they were in could provide.

Much of Sebastian's time during the touring years was spent with his father, for usually, wherever they happened to be, it was his father who drove him to his fiddle lessons and stayed to listen while he worked. And during Rest Periods, it was his father who took him to whatever music school he was attending. Then too, of course, even when he was not himself playing his father was with Sebastian at all rehearsals and concerts. So Sebastian and his father were great friends but this did not mean David was sure what

Sebastian was thinking. This worried him, so sometimes he talked to Sebastian about the life he led, trying to find out if he was happy or if he would rather live in one place and play at no more concerts until he was grown up.

'You've made an awful lot of money, old man, and though part of it has to go on the rest of us, much of it is banked for you. You could give all this up at any time if you wanted to and still afford first-class lessons.'

Sebastian was not the right person to say that sort of thing to. He was happy playing the fiddle and when he was playing at a concert, or at rehearsals, he was like a grown-up musician for he never thought of himself except as a musician amongst musicians. He could not help knowing other musicians thought he was unusual, for orchestras would often subscribe money to buy him a present. These presents were rather odd for a small boy for they were usually silver plaques or what is called a canteen of silver, but Sebastian was pleased because musicians had given them to him, and, anyhow, he never used the presents for as they could not be transported round the world they were put away in banks. But away from rehearsals, concerts and fiddle lessons Sebastian was the quietest and shyest of the family, liking, in the very little time he had to himself, to play childish family games like Snap or Spillikins. So when his father talked about the money he earned, or giving up touring, Sebastian wriggled away from answering. What happened to children was a grown-up thing and was not the sort of subject he thought a father ought to talk about.

It was not until the third touring year that enough was said by Myra, Wolfgang and Ethel out loud to make them begin to see they were all thinking the same sort of thing. It was another autumn. Myra was twelve, Sebastian eleven, Wolfgang ten and Ethel nearly eight and a half. They were in the middle of a European tour and had just arrived in Venice. They were staying in a hotel where they used an extra sitting-room as a schoolroom. Miss Popple was giving a literature lesson.

'We're going to read *The Merchant of Venice* this autumn,' she said. 'Such fun reading it for the first time here, isn't it?'

'Why is here fun?' Wolfgang asked.

'I meant actually reading the story of the Merchant while we are in Venice,' Miss Popple explained. 'Don't you think that's interesting?'

Wolfgang looked surprised.

'Are we in Venice? I didn't know.'

'But of course you knew, dear,' said Miss Popple. 'Look out of the window at the canal.'

'Or smell it,' Ethel suggested.

Wolfgang dismissed Venice with a gesture.

'All right, so we're in Venice. But who cares?'

Miss Popple tried to look shocked but inside she knew she was beginning to feel 'who cares-ish' herself about places.

'It can happen,' said Myra. 'I thought we were in Pisa when it was Milan.'

Ethel laid a comforting hand on Miss Popple's arm.

'Popps, dear, towns do look all alike.'

That day they went on reading *The Merchant of Venice* but, because they had admitted that one country was beginning to look exactly like another, it was as if a small wall had been broken down. Their mother and father and people they met had always said what lucky children they were to learn geography by travel and not from an atlas, so, like many things said by grown-ups, they had believed it to be true. But now that Wolfgang had owned he did not know or care that he was in Venice, and they had all agreed it was often difficult to remember where they were, it had – if not destroyed the idea they were lucky – at least made them wonder if children who stayed at home, with atlases, were so much worse off.

Perhaps something would have been said earlier had not the longed-for 'Next Year' dangled before their noses. Next Year was the year when Sebastian would be twelve and so at last permitted to have a licence to play at concerts in England. Whenever they were anywhere near Polly and David had flown to England to visit their parents. But the children never went, so by the autumn of Next Year it would be four years since they had seen a grandfather or a grandmother.

'Which is not nice, Popps,' Myra confided to Miss Popple. 'For in proper families grandparents are visited after church on Sundays.'

Because the grandparents did not think it nice either it had been decided the family would arrive in England at the end of July to spend all August with Grandfather and Grandmother in Devonshire. From the moment this plan was thought of, long before it got on to Mr Ruttenstein's list called 'fixtures', it was almost the children's only topic of conversation.

'There's a little lane, sort of sandy, with dear little ferns sticking out of the banks like tongues,' Myra said. 'It goes down to the sea. I'm going to take Wag down it every single day.'

Sebastian could almost smell the little lane.

'I'm going down it every day too. It has simply enormous wild strawberries growing in it.'

Wolfgang could not remember the lane but he remembered other things.

'I was only small when I was last there so I wasn't allowed much in case I'd be sick. But always there's lashings of Devonshire cream. I'm not small now and I shall eat it and eat it and eat it.'

Even Ethel had memories.

'Didn't we catch shrimps?'

'We did,' Myra agreed. 'But though you tried you never caught any.'

Ethel made a face at her.

'I shall this time. I'll catch more than any of you.'

'Can you imagine?' said Myra. 'Four whole weeks in a house which is almost ours. I simply can't.'

They all tried but it was too difficult.

'I suppose,' Wolfgang suggested, 'at our grandfather's we'll still have to be careful about sand on bedroom floors and all those things you are in hired houses.'

But Myra and Sebastian remembered the rectory better than that.

'Not a bit of it, Wolf,' said Sebastian. 'I once dropped a whole bowl of eggs – they've got hens – in the hall and all Grandmother said was, "I'll scoop them up. They'll do for cooking."'

Myra looked at Ethel.

'And you, Ettie, though you won't remember because you were only just five, got tar on your sandals and it stuck to the drawing-room carpet, but Granny wasn't a bit cross. She said she'd get it off with butter.'

Miss Popple was just as excited as the children, for while the family were in Devonshire she was to stay with Dan and Mary.

'They've always kept my room for me. I can't wait to see their babies. Dan says little Tom is like him, but Ann's the image of me. Tom's my godson, as you know. I daren't think about it I'm so excited.'

When Miss Popple talked like that there was usually a little pause before anyone said anything because if Miss Popple was going to Dan's cottage she would see Apple Bough. Usually one of them would show where all their thoughts had jumped to when they said:

'That funny mixed red and white rose should have flowers,' or 'I wonder if there's still raspberries under the nettles.'

Mumsmum and Mumsdad would not need a special visit for their flat was in St John's Wood, which was the part of London where David had rented a house for September until Christmas, which was when Sebastian would be giving concerts in England.

'I can't see,' Ethel would grumble to Myra, 'why we can't spend all the winter in London. You could have Wag with you and I could go every day to the same dancing school. Why do we have to have our Rest Period in San Francisco?'

Myra sometimes dreamed that plans were changed and they did have their Rest Period in London, but she knew it was a wishing sort of dreaming.

'Misken, I suppose. Anyway, it's convenient for Mr Ruttenstein.'

Ethel would answer in a savage whisper.

'I'm beginning to hate Mr Ruttenstein. I don't think he ever thinks of us as people but just as Sebastian's relations.'

Myra had to be fair.

'Well, to him that's all we are. What I keep hoping is that as England is so small almost everywhere is an "overnight", so the rest of us may be allowed to stop in London while Sebastian goes to places like Manchester and Birmingham.'

Ethel might be the youngest but she was the most realistic of the Forums.

'You've another think coming. Someone will say: "Such a pity for the children to miss seeing Manchester. They may not have another chance." Anyway, Mummy would be sure to make a fuss about breaking up the family.'

'It won't be too awful even if we do have to go to places with Sebastian. I wrote to Dan and he said dogs can travel in ordinary carriages on British Railways.'

The other three were nervous when Myra made too many plans for Wag, it would be so awful if they did not come true.

'Don't count on Wag coming. Lots of hotels won't have dogs.'

But Myra had every plan made.

'Sebastian is going to pretend he's his. You know how nobody ever says "no" to him.'

That winter they spent a Rest Period in Paris. Mr Ruttenstein had arranged it partly so that Sebastian could study with Dermidoff but largely because they were what he called 'placed right' for the spring and summer tour of Germany, the Scandinavian countries and Russia. As it happened, only of course Mr Ruttenstein would not know about that, Paris suited not only Sebastian but Wolfgang and Ethel as well. Wolfgang because of the music school at which he was taking classes. He told Myra about it.

'I'm doing composition and I've absolutely decided I'm going to write pop songs. The sort that gets into the top ten.'

Myra gazed at him in horror.

'Wolf, you can't! I should think Daddy would drop dead. You know what he thinks about that sort of music.'

There were two pianos in the apartment they had rented that year. Wolfgang, making sure the door was shut, went to one and played a tune.

'It's no good making a face, Myra. I think it's a lovely tune, all goo and I like goo. You've got to be interested because I can't tell anyone else. Popps doesn't know the difference between this and Bach, and Ettie is only interested in dancing.'

'I am interested if that's truly the sort of noise you want to make,' Myra could not call it music, 'but I think it's pure slop. I bet if anybody puts words to it they will be about love and the moon and things like that.'

Wolfgang looked pleased.

'You're so right. I'm planning to find a song competition and go in for it.'

'Wolf! You wouldn't! Think what Daddy would feel. Sebastian's brother writing stuff like that.'

Wolfgang slammed the piano shut.

'Don't you start. We aren't just Sebastian's brother and

sisters. We're people.' He thumped his chest. 'I'm Wolf. A whole boy. And if I like to write songs that win competitions I shall write them. When Monsieur Moulin read what I've just played to you he didn't make faces, he said I was a clever little cabbage and he'd give me extra lessons.'

Myra was glad Wolfgang was liking Paris.

'Well, don't play that sort of tune when Daddy's about. You don't want to spoil things. Remember Devonshire's This Year now.'

That winter Ethel had been taking her first real ballet lessons. She went to a famous teacher called Madame Leninskya, feeling very grand in a white tunic, tights and pink satin shoes. She enjoyed her classes enormously for she had learnt dancing from various teachers since she was five, so had been well grounded in simple exercises based on the five positions. She had been to classes with Madame Leninskya before, but in other years had only been allowed to attend the baby classes, and both she and Myra had learnt character dancing. But now in the general class she found she was somebody. She was always telling Myra about it.

'Of course I'm not allowed to work on my pointes yet. Madame says not till next winter when I'm nine and a half, but I do everything else the others do and I'm always being pulled out to do things alone.'

'A photographer came to the studio today to photograph us and, do you know, Madame made me take off my shoes to show him proper dancer's feet.'

Myra was glad for Ethel that she was so happy, though she was not interested in dancing herself. She thought

60

the character class she had to attend once a week more than enough.

'Has Madame ever said you were good?'

Ethel was shocked.

'Madame would never say a thing like that to a child. All she says is work, work, work and never be satisfied, but I can see the other girls think Madame sort of picks me out. If only I could go on learning from her instead of going on tour.'

Myra had felt nervous twinges in her inside ever since Next Year had become This Year. Everything about This Year, at least until after England, had to be perfect.

'Don't talk like that, Ettie, you know it can't happen. Anyway, I'm sure the tour will pass faster than any tour ever has because we've Devonshire coming.'

Then one morning, just before the Rest Period came to an end, a letter arrived from Mr Ruttenstein. There were letters from him so often nobody was particularly interested. Then David made a startled sort of noise.

'It looks as if we shan't make Devonshire this summer.'

Four pairs of eyes were turned to him. Myra asked in a whisper:

'Why?'

David looked at Sebastian.

'You knew Misken had written a concerto and dedicated it to you, I suppose?'

That was the sort of question Sebastian hated for Misken never said anything straight out. If you were a pupil of his, it was more from the half-said things that you knew what he meant.

'Sort of.'

'It seems it is to have its first performance in Hollywood early in September. He wants you to play of course.'

'How absolutely enchanting!' said Polly. 'It's easily arranged, we can fly to Hollywood after the Russian tour, then on to London in time for Sebastian's first concert.'

David was so thrilled for Sebastian he could hardly speak.

'This is incredible news! You are a lucky boy, Sebastian! Imagine having Misken's concerto dedicated to you!'

Myra, Wolfgang and Ethel gazed hopefully at Sebastian. Would he say he would rather go to Devonshire? Just once would he say a thing like that? But as they watched his face they knew the answer and they could not blame him. It was a terrific honour for a boy who would not be twelve until August to have a concerto dedicated to him by Misken, and it would be frightfully rude to write and say you couldn't come and play it because you'd rather be in Devonshire. For the same sort of reasons somehow the other three held in what they were thinking. It is difficult to be the one to make a scene when your father and mother think the most wonderful thing in the world has just happened. But directly breakfast was over Myra, Wolfgang and Ethel rushed into the schoolroom and slammed the door.

'How I hate Mr Ruttenstein,' Wolfgang stormed. 'He makes me feel like a parcel that's always in the post.'

Ethel lay across the table and beat on it with her fists.

'No Devonshire! Devonshire was an absolute promise. I bet if Misken knew he'd let someone else play the fiddle instead of Sebastian.'

Wolfgang stamped round the room.

'We're not people at all to Mr Ruttenstein. It's as if Sebastian was a dog and we were his tail.'

There was a small silence after Wolfgang had said that during which he and Ethel tried not to look at Myra. It was worse for her than any of them. To bring Wag from Devonshire to London as part of the family could have happened. But to send for him to live in a rented London house would be more difficult. Somebody was sure to say dogs were better in the country. In the silence the sound of Sebastian practising his fiddle in his bedroom came into the room. Myra looked towards the sound.

'It's not his fault. He can't help being a musical prodigy.' Ethel slid off the table.

'Of course he can't. But I wish he'd stand up to Mr Ruttenstein more. He's the only one who can.'

Myra, thinking of Devonshire and Wag, found she had a lump in her throat. She tried to get rid of it but it was no good, her voice would only come out with a wobble, and two tears trickled down her cheeks.

'He's the only one. But he'll never do it. Let's all put it in our prayers to ask for Devonshire to be possible next year.'

At that moment Miss Popple came in. She heard what Myra said and she saw the tears.

'I should not wonder if Devonshire were possible this year. I am just on my way to tell your parents that I am not changing my plans. I shall stay with Dan and Mary while Sebastian is in Hollywood.'

If a cat had stood on its hind legs and announced a change of plans the children would not have been more surprised. They gaped at Miss Popple, seeing her for the first time as a person with a life of her own and not just as their governess. She looked as apple-ish as usual and as cosy but somehow taller, and there was a special sort of glint in her eyes. Then she smiled, and she had a lovely smile, and they smiled too. It was as if it had been a wet day and suddenly the sun had come out. It was impossible to imagine the family beginning to get to Hollywood, let alone arriving there, without Miss Popple to supervise all the arrangements.

Ethel turned a pirouette.

'It will be difficult for Mummy to remember everything even for just her, Daddy and Sebastian.'

Wolfgang rushed at Miss Popple and hugged her.

'Most glorious Popps! They won't want us without you. When Mummy says families shouldn't separate she's thinking of you as family.'

Miss Popple looked at Myra.

'Stop worrying, dear. I can see you with Wag in Devonshire, and when I see things they nearly always come true.'

6

Devonshire

Devonshire with Wag did come true and was so gorgeous
that afterwards, when Myra, Wolfgang or Ethel wanted a
word to describe something perfect they would say, 'It was
Devonshire.' Perhaps Devonshire seemed extra nice because
all the Forums had been so miserable in the weeks before
the children went there. When arranging Devonshire it
had of course been planned that all the family would be
there, and at first, even when it was known David, Polly
and Sebastian would be in America, it still seemed as if
August would be a glorious month. But as August got nearer
and nearer doubts arose. It started with Polly. Suddenly
she stopped rushing off to work in somebody's studio and
instead hung about the schoolroom looking like a cat who
has lost her kittens. And she, who was always so vague,
made a list of rules and added to it each day, things like:
'Never eat berries out of the hedges unless you are absolutely
certain what they are.' 'Always carry a jersey. The weather
in England can be very cold in August.'

The trouble was, of course, that the family had never separated before so as the time for parting got nearer August began to look like the 'monstrous crow, as black as a tar-barrel.'

'It will be awfully odd being just us three,' Myra said to Miss Popple. 'I wish I could remember Granny and Grandfather better. Four years is an awfully long time not to have seen people.'

Miss Popple was not worried about the three in Devonshire, she was thinking about Sebastian.

'I do hope your father and mother see Sebastian gets to bed early. When they get talking about music they forget how time passes.'

'It's queer,' Wolfgang explained to Myra. 'You want something and want something then, when you get it, you start wondering whether you'll like it.'

Ethel was openly nervous.

'It's all very well for you and Wolf,' she told Myra, 'but I was only a child when I last met Granny and Grandfather so I don't remember them. I keep thinking, suppose I hate them.'

David knew about all the fussing that was going on but he was busy with Sebastian's concerts and thought it was only natural Polly should be in a state at parting with the children, but that she would feel better as soon as they got to Hollywood. But when Sebastian showed he was sharing the general gloom he decided it was time he said something.

They were in Moscow, which should have been an exciting experience for they had not been to Russia before. Musically it was perfect; the orchestra with whom Sebastian was playing was superb, and in Russia there was no fuss about the number or length of rehearsals, so hours passed making music. But outside the concert hall none of the family were finding Russian ways easy. They had an enormous suite in the hotel, which should have been nice but in Russia you did not ring a bell and waiters came running; there was no bell and if you spoke on the telephone it was to the reception desk where they spoke only Russian. So the whole family had to troop down to the dining-room for meals. Feeling depressed anyway, the dining-room made them feel worse. It was full of aspidistras, Nottingham lace and blue velvet. Time means nothing in Russia so it was usual to wait for as much as an hour before getting anything to eat, and even at the best of moments that would have been a strain, but when all the family could think about was that in two weeks' time they would be thousands of miles apart, waiting became unbearable.

To make things worse, none of the family liked Russian food and it actually made Myra and Miss Popple sick. For what suited Russians, they discovered, was rather greasy food on to which was poured sour cream. To make it more difficult to eat, everything you ordered was put on the table at once, so while they hurriedly drank their soup the other course was getting cold with fat clinging round the plate. To feel sick as well as miserable is the end.

It was a Saturday when David spoke up. There was to be a concert that evening but the day was free.

'What would you like to do, all of you? How about a Park of Culture and Rest? I believe we can lunch there.'

'Not for me, thank you,' said Wolfgang. 'We ate lunch in one on Monday. It was absolutely raw smoked salmon.'

'Oh, don't, Wolf,' Myra groaned. 'I was sick again last night.'

David tried something else.

'How about Lenin's tomb?'

'Look out of the window,' said Ethel. 'There's a queue miles and miles long.'

David was determined to get them out.

'Well, how about a walk? It's a beautiful city. Look at the cupolas shining in the sun.'

'It's best to be frank,' said Wolfgang. 'None of us wants to do anything.'

'I think,' Polly put in, 'we're all a bit depressed.'

'That's it, Daddy,' Sebastian agreed. 'You don't feel like sightseeing when you're miserable.'

There were three grand pianos in their sitting-room. David had been sitting on the stool by one picking out tunes with one hand while he talked. Now he got up and stood where he could see all the family.

'This has got to stop. You're all being very silly and that goes for you too, Polly. We might be going to part for years instead of just one month.'

'Five weeks with travelling,' said Sebastian.

'Five most exciting weeks for all of us. We're going to have the excitement of being the first to hear the Misken concerto, and you three are going to have a glorious holiday with my father and mother, now what is there to moan about?'

Put that way it did seem rather idiotic.

'It's because we've never been by ourselves before,' Myra explained.

'Very lucky for us,' David agreed. 'But that's no reason to go about looking as if a tragedy had hit us. Now run along and put on your things, all of you. I don't want to see another long face.'

After that, though they all felt a bit wormy when they thought of separation day, they stopped looking miserable, and though Polly and Myra had tears in their eyes when they said goodbye they were ashamed they were there, for David was right – five weeks was not long. Besides, it was impossible for Myra to feel miserable for long for at London airport Dan would be waiting with Wag.

Myra had been afraid Wag would have forgotten her, but the moment she called out 'Wag! Wag!' he was out of Dan's arms and streaking so fast towards her his legs did not seem to touch the ground.

Most of Devonshire lived up to what Myra and Wolfgang had remembered about it, but there were some nice things they had not expected. One of the best was that they could go where they liked alone, something which was never allowed when they were on tour.

'What are you three doing this morning?' Grandfather had asked at their first breakfast.

'Could we bathe?' Wolfgang had suggested.

'Why not?' Grandfather had got up. 'Go in about eleven, you'll find the sea full of summer visitors at that time, which will cover my promise to your mother not to let you bathe unless there are strong swimmers about.'

No one likes to look silly so somehow nothing was said and presently, feeling incredibly venturesome, Wag, and the three children with their bathing things rolled in towels, were running down the lane, which was just as they remembered it, ferns, wild strawberries and all, on their way to the sea.

Naturally, as the days passed and they got used to it, the niceness of going where you liked alone wore off, but what never wore off was the surprisingness of Grandfather. In their minds the children had thought of him as old, but though he looked oldish they discovered he did not think or talk old and in Devonshire a great deal of talking went on, especially after tea before the children went to bed. To begin with, both Granny and Grandfather wanted to know all about how they lived on tour, but one night Grandfather started asking questions about themselves.

'I know your father loves all this travelling.'

'Always did want to travel, even when he was a little boy,' Grandmother put in.

'But how about your mother?' Grandfather asked. 'Isn't she getting sick of it yet?'

Myra was thinking of words to explain when Wolfgang said:

'No, Mummy likes it even more than Daddy. It's her that thinks it's nice for us to be world citizens.'

'So wonderful for the children to learn geography by travel and not from an atlas,' Ethel quoted.

'And do you three agree with that?' Grandfather asked.

'Not me,' said Wolfgang. 'I'm beginning to abhor travelling.'

Myra had Wag on her knee. She leant down to kiss him.

'But we shall always have to, of course, I mean, you can't split up a family, can you?'

Grandmother looked thoughtfully at Myra.

'It's not desirable, but I suppose if Sebastian goes on touring it will have to happen sooner or later. There's proper education for you three to be thought about.'

'We're pretty well educated,' Wolfgang said. 'Popps has diplomas and things and whenever there's a Rest Period extra people teach us.'

'We know all about that,' Grandfather agreed. 'But how about Ettie here? Can you learn your dancing properly if you're always moving, Ettie?'

Ettie had been practising some frappés holding on to Grandfather's desk. Now she came and sat on his knee.

'You know I learned proper dancing with Madame Leninskya in Paris last winter. Well, after my last lesson she sent for me.'

Wolfgang leant over the back of Grandfather's chair.

'Ettie was scared stiff for nobody ever saw Madame Leninskya alone before.'

Ettie turned to look up at Grandfather.

'Sometimes they do but not often. I remembered to make an awfully good curtsy.'

Grandmother found Myra and Ethel's bobs on greeting people charming.

'And very nicely you can do it, dear.'

'Not just a bob, a down-to-the-ground one,' Myra explained.

'What did this Madame what's-it want?' Grandfather asked.

'To know what was planned for me because she thought I ought soon to settle with one teacher, she said I needed the discipline.'

'Did she now.' Grandfather played with Ettie's hair. 'And what did you say to that?'

'What could she say?' Myra asked. 'How can she learn from one teacher the way we live?'

Wolfgang broke in.

'But you hear what Madame Leninskya said next.'

Grandmother looked up from the jersey she was knitting. 'Tell us, Ettie.'

Ettie got off Grandfather's knee and gave an imitation of Madame.

'I think when you are in London, my child, your parents should apply for an audition for you at The Royal Ballet School.' Ethel dropped her voice to an awed whisper. 'Then she said: "I shall of course write to Dame Ninette de Valois about you."'

Grandmother laid down her knitting.

'Did she now, and what did you say?'

Ethel made a despairing gesture.

'What could I say? She's not a person to listen to excuses. To her that she thinks I have talent is all that matters. So I just made another curtsy like this' – Ethel curtsied beautifully – 'and said I'd tell Daddy.'

'And did you?' Grandfather asked.

A cry which sounded as if somebody had dug a pin into her burst out of Ethel.

'Of course I didn't. What was the good?'

Myra, carrying Wag, came over to Grandmother and sat at her feet.

'We don't suppose Madame meant talent like Sebastian has. Anyway, you can't be sure with a dancer, things can go wrong. How could Ettie ask Daddy to make Sebastian stop touring just for her?'

Ethel came back to Grandfather and lolled against him.

'Imagine me at The Royal Ballet School with a letter about me from Madame Leninskya! But it's a Cinderella-at-the-ball sort of thing – it can never happen.'

That evening Grandfather did not ask any more questions, but a few nights later he started again. This time it was Wolfgang he wanted to know about.

'What are you going to be when you grow up, Wolf?'

The lavender had been picked and Grandmother and the three children were filling little muslin bags with it. Filling bags with lavender was something they always remembered about Devonshire for they never did it anywhere else. Grandmother's drawing-room was so full of the rich oily scent that it was making the children drowsy. But asked a question like that and Wolfgang was wide awake.

'You won't like it when I tell you.'

'And why won't I?' Grandfather asked.

'It's not your sort of thing. I mean, your choir sings proper good music always.'

'You should hear them at our musical festival,' said Grandmother, 'lovely that is.'

But Grandfather was interested in Wolfgang.

'Do I gather your ambition is to do with bad music?'

'Don't ask him, Grandfather,' Myra pleaded. 'You and Granny will simply hate it.'

Grandfather chuckled.

'You let me be the judge of that. Come on, Wolf, what is this ambition?'

73

Wolfgang laid down the bag he was filling and went to the piano, opened it and sat down on the music stool.

'I'm going to write pop songs. This is the one I'm working on now.'

It was a new tune that even Myra had not heard. Though no one could call it highbrow it was pretty in a goo-y way.

'Thank you,' said Grandfather when Wolfgang stopped playing. 'Not to my taste but no doubt it will please others.'

Myra was amazed.

'But you don't think he ought to write that sort of music? Daddy would simply hate it if he knew.'

Grandfather thought about that, then he asked:

'Does your Miss Popple teach you Scripture?'

The children were shocked that Grandfather should suppose she did not.

'Of course,' said Ethel.

'Three times a week,' Myra added.

'But since the last Rest Period she calls it religious instruction because of us getting older,' Wolfgang explained.

'Good,' said Grandfather, 'then you know the parable about the servants to whom their master gave talents?'

The children looked doubtful. Ethel shook her head.

'That's a dodgy one.'

'You rather pounced that at us,' Myra complained. 'I expect we do know it really only you don't expect to be asked Scripture questions on a holiday.'

But Wolfgang had suddenly remembered.

'One man had five and he made it ten. One had two and he made it four. But the silly idiot who had only one just shoved it in the ground, so of course he still had only one when his boss came back.'

Grandfather looked pleased.

'Well done! We are like those servants, you know. We all start with so many talents and some day we must account for what we did with them.'

'Goodness!' said Myra. 'I should think Sebastian started with at least a hundred.'

Grandmother smiled.

'And he's turning them into another hundred, bless him.'

Ethel looked up from her lavender.

'Let's face it, he's got a better chance than us.'

'That's really what I was coming to,' Grandfather explained. 'Often we have to make our own chances. If Wolf's talent does turn out to be for writing popular music, it will be up to him to write the best popular music that it is in him to write, and up to him to give his talent every chance.' Then, just as he had done when he talked to Ethel about her dancing, he changed the subject.

Grandfather's questions had a stirring up effect on the children. It is exciting to be thought about as a person with a talent when always you have only been the sisters and brother of somebody with a talent. As they went down the lane to bathe, or on picnics to pick blackberries, they puzzled what Grandfather was getting at.

'Of course he doesn't understand about dancing,' Ethel said one morning. 'Nobody, not even Madame Leninskya, would say it was important I went to The Royal Ballet School now. Actually, I think just nine would be too young.

But I do think an audition would be a good idea to see if they would have me next year.'

'How would it?' Wolf asked. 'You couldn't go. By this time next year we most likely won't be anywhere near England.'

Myra fumbled for the words she wanted.

'I think – I mean I'm almost sure that's what Grandfather meant. I think he wants us to do things about ourselves.' She spoke in a rush for what she wanted to say was so much the opposite to anything they had ever felt. 'I think, even if you can never go to The Royal Ballet School, you ought to ask Madame Leninskya to write that letter.'

They were in the middle of the lane to the sea. Wolfgang gave a dramatic stagger and fell against the bank.

'Myra Forum! Did you mean Ettie should have an audition without telling Daddy and Mummy?'

Myra nodded.

'Get started anyway. You see, I think they can't imagine us not always travelling like we do now, but Grandfather can. I think Ettie finding out if the school would have her is a thing we could do. Then, if the school says yes, we could all try and think of a way for her to go to it.'

'Goodness!' gasped Ettie. 'Do you suppose there is a way? It's a boarding school. I suppose that would help.'

Wolfgang got up off the bank.

'If you learn to dance at a school I shall find a school which teaches me to write songs, and it will be a boarding school too.'

'I don't think there is a school like that, Wolf,' Myra said. 'But if there is what would happen to me, I wonder?'

Ethel slipped an arm through Myra's.

'You'll go to a school too. One that takes dogs as well as girls.'

This was such a lovely picture that it made them all laugh, and by the time they stopped laughing they were on the beach and the future was out of their minds.

It was noticeable, Myra thought, that though Grandfather often after that spoke about Ethel's dancing or Wolfgang's songs he never questioned her about her talents. 'And a good thing too,' she confided to Wag, 'for though Grandfather says we all start with talents mine are what Popps would call conspicuous by their absence.'

Then one afternoon when August was coming to an end Myra was in the garden when Grandfather came out of the rectory carrying a pile of church magazines.

'Come and help me deliver these,' he suggested.

Myra called Wag and skipped to his side.

'I can because Wolf and Ettie are watching cream made.'

Grandfather smiled down at her.

'Given you an afternoon off, have they?'

Myra grinned up at him for she knew he was teasing.

'I generally do what they do, they're still young, you know.'

Grandfather laid a hand on Myra's shoulder.

'Your Granny and I are going to be very lonely people after you three go. I shall especially miss you, Myra.'

Myra was amazed for she could not help knowing that after Sebastian it was Wolfgang or Ethel people were usually interested in.

'Me! But I'm so dull. I don't do anything.'

'Talents don't have to be for one of the arts. You can have a talent for wisdom and being a good sister.'

Myra laughed.

'I've no wisdom. You ask Popps. Everybody's better at sums than me.'

Grandfather looked fondly at Myra. He thought her a most attractive child with her serious face, the dark hair held back in an Alice-in-Wonderland band.

'There is all kinds of wisdom. I think it's your wisdom that is going to find the way to put the brake on all this travelling.'

Myra felt this was a chance to make Grandfather face facts.

'I never have thought you quite understood about us. Unless Sebastian does it nobody can stop us travelling. You see, Daddy likes Sebastian to play at concerts, but Mummy won't let Sebastian go anywhere without her, and she won't leave us behind. She was in a terrible flap before they went to Hollywood.'

'I know all that,' Grandfather said calmly, 'but I don't believe because plans are made they can't be changed. I have felt, and so has Granny, that it's time you three asserted yourselves. You make a wise plan, Myra, and you'll find your father will fall in with it.'

Myra sighed.

'I know Daddy is your son. But I think you've forgotten him rather. He goes anywhere because of music, and he's terribly vague, we'd have lost him dozens of times if Popps and I hadn't looked after him. He's not the sort of person you talk plans to.'

'I know all that, which is why I want you to assert yourself. There must be something you want to do more than trail round the earth behind Sebastian.'

Myra knew the answer to that.

'I'd like to live in the country with Wag, but that's more a dream than a plan, isn't it?'

Grandfather stopped walking.

'I could have a talk with your father, but he and your mother, when I last saw them, were so convinced that not only was the life you led the best for you children but that you liked it, that I'd have a job getting him to see the other side of the picture. I think this touring has become such a habit with your parents that there won't be a halt unless you children find the reason for it.'

'You mean a reason like Ettie's dancing? But she thinks if they take her it is more likely next autumn than this.'

Grandfather pointed to a cottage.

'We leave a magazine there. When you decide that the time has come to have a regular home, and honestly mean it, a way will be shown you to make it happen.'

Myra knew Grandfather never said things without meaning them, but that was a startling statement.

'I feel like the French peasants must have felt when they were planning the Revolution.'

'So you should,' said Grandfather, 'for this is a sort of revolution, only it's not my idea that anybody should be hurt by it. Now take this magazine and push it under the door. Mrs Tippett, who lives in that cottage, won't be in, she goes to see her daughter on Wednesday afternoons.'

7

The Man in the Train

Leaving Devonshire was not so awful as the children
had been afraid it would be. Of course saying goodbye to
Grandfather, Granny and all the friends they had made was
not nice, but at the London station to meet them would be
Popps. Then, in five days' time, the rest of the family would
arrive from Hollywood. Then there were Mumsmum and
Mumsdad to see, let alone the house which would be their
home until Christmas.

'Goodbye, dear, darling Grandfather and Granny,' Ethel
said. 'I think staying with you has been the nicest thing that
ever happened to me.'

'It's been superb,' Wolfgang agreed.

'And you'll come to London to hear Sebastian, won't
you?' Myra pleaded.

Grandfather leant through the carriage window.

'More likely we'll hear him in Bath. We're not fond
of London.'

Grandmother pressed her face in beside his.

'And when we do go we don't travel first-class like you luxurious children.'

'We're only doing it because Mummy thinks it's safer.' Ethel looked over her shoulder and spoke in a whisper. 'Only one man and he doesn't come out from behind his paper.'

A whistle blew. Grandfather and Grandmother stood back.

'Goodbye! Goodbye! Be sure to eat all the lunch.'

The children and Wag went into the carriage. Wolfgang looked up at the lunch basket Grandmother had packed for them.

'I wish Granny hadn't said that about lunch. It's made me hungry. It's hours since breakfast.'

'It isn't, you know, Wolf,' Myra said firmly. 'It only feels it because we started early to drive to Taunton.'

'It's not me that's feeling it, it's my stomach,' Wolfgang argued. 'Don't you think a little snack would be a good idea?'

'One sandwich each,' Ethel suggested. 'They're filled with Devonshire cream and strawberry jam.'

Myra weakened.

'If I open the basket will you absolutely promise you won't take more than one? You know how Popps says snacks between meals spoil your appetite.'

While Myra was undoing the basket Wolfgang and Ethel made faces at each other and looked at the newspaper which hid the man in the corner.

'Poor beast!' their faces said. 'It seems mean to eat when he's got nothing.' Myra was sitting opposite. Wolfgang gave her a gende kick.

'"Little Birds are feeding – Justices with jam."'

Myra was puzzled.

'What?'

Wolfgang made a face in the direction of the newspaper.

'Feeding Justices with jam,' he said, emphasising the word jam.

Myra had put their sandwiches on a cardboard plate. She nodded and added a fourth and passed the plate to Wolfgang.

'You do it,' she whispered.

Wolfgang got up. He spoke to the back of the paper.

'Excuse me, sir, but would you like a sandwich?'

The paper was lowered and a youngish man with twinkling grey-blue eyes looked at Ethel.

'Cream with strawberry jam, I think you said.'

'Were you listening?' Wolfgang was surprised. 'You looked so busy reading.'

The man took a sandwich and smiled at them all.

'I always listen, it comes natural to me.'

'Talking is what comes naturally to me,' said Wolfgang.

'And quoting, I gather.' The man took a bite of sandwich. 'Very nice too. Where does "Little Birds are feeding – Justices with jam" come from?'

'It's Lewis Carroll,' Myra explained. 'We know it because it comes in a book of nonsense rhymes we were given in New York.'

'It wasn't New York, Myra,' Ethel objected. 'It was San Francisco.'

'How does the rest of it go?' the man asked.

Wolfgang dismissed the rest of the rhyme with a gesture.

'There's far too much of it. It starts:

'"Little Birds are dining
        Warily and well
        Hid in mossy cell:
Hid, I say, by waiters
Gorgeous in their gaiters—
        I've a tale to tell."'

'I like that part about gorgeous in their gaiters,' the man said. 'Is there anything else unusual in the book?'

'Say that nice one about dandelions,' Ethel suggested.

'It's a Christina Rossetti,' Myra said, 'but you'd never guess it.'

Wolfgang did not care what he recited as long as people listened to him doing it.

'"When fishes set umbrellas up
        If the rain-drops run,
Lizards will want their parasols
        To shade them from the sun.

The peacock has a score of eyes,
        With which he cannot see;
The cod-fish has a silent sound,
        However that may be.

No dandelions tell the time,
        Although they turn to clocks;
Cat's cradle does not hold the cat,
        Nor foxglove fit the fox."'

'We like the last verse best,' said Myra. 'It's nice, "Nor foxglove fit the fox," isn't it?'

The man had finished his sandwich. He wiped his fingers and nodded in agreement. Then he spoke to Wolfgang.

'Do you know any other poetry – I mean that isn't nonsense?'

Wolfgang made a gesture with both arms.

'Tons! Popps – that's our governess, her real name is Miss Popple – makes us learn heaps, she says it gives us something to think about on journeys.'

The man laughed.

'That's an unusual reason for learning poetry. Have you got any favourites?'

'We all like "O to be in England",' said Myra. 'Do you know that one?'

The man nodded.

'Browning. He called it "Home thoughts, from Abroad".'

'We know,' Myra agreed. 'You see, he was like us, always away.'

'When we were very young,' Ethel explained, 'we lived in England. So we know about how "the lowest boughs and the brushwood sheaf" should look.'

Wolfgang made an expressive face to the man.

'She doesn't remember really, she just thinks she does. She had only been five for three months when we went away.'

'Could you recite it?' the man asked. 'I've forgotten it a bit.'

'You shouldn't encourage him,' Myra protested. 'He's an awful show-off.'

Wolfgang paid no attention to that. He was quite

unself-conscious, and anyway, the whole family spoke poetry well, respecting the music in the lines.

> '"O to be in England
> Now that April's there.
> And whoever wakes in England
> Sees, some morning, unaware,
> That the lowest boughs and the brushwood sheaf
> Round the elm-tree bole are in tiny leaf,
> While the chaffinch sings on the orchard bough
> In England – now!
>
> And after April, when May follows,
> And the whitethroat builds, and all the swallows!
> Hark, where my blossom'd pear-tree in the hedge
> Leans to the field and scatters on the clover
> Blossoms and dewdrops – at the bent spray's edge –
> That's the wise thrush; he sings each song
>   twice over,
> Lest you should think he never could recapture
> The first fine careless rapture!
> And though the fields look rough with hoary dew,
> All will be gay when noontide wakes anew
> The buttercups, the little children's dower
> —Far brighter than this gaudy melon-flower!"'

'I must say,' Ethel admitted, 'you said that very nicely, Wolf.'

'Almost it hurts,' Myra explained to the man. 'You see, our house – Apple Bough it was called – was full of buttercups and all the things Browning said. So we know just how he felt about melon-flowers. You can get too much of jacarandas and those sort of flowers, can't you?'

Before the man could answer the carriage door was thrown open and an attendant from the restaurant-car looked in.

'Luncheon tickets?' he asked.

The man said:

'Second sitting, please.'

But by now he was a friend. Grandmother always packed lunch for double the number of people who were going to eat it.

'Don't go to the restaurant. Share ours,' Myra invited.

'Cornish pasties, hard-boiled eggs and bits of chicken,' Wolfgang urged.

Ethel had seen how much the sandwich was enjoyed.

'And more jam and cream sandwiches.'

The man hesitated.

'Will you have enough?'

'Heaps.' Myra smiled at the attendant. 'You don't mind, do you? I'm sure somebody else will use his ticket.'

'As I'm staying to lunch,' said the man, 'I ought to introduce myself. I am Owen Oslip.'

He said this in a way that made Myra think they ought to have heard of him. As it seemed rude to admit they had not she hurriedly introduced themselves.

'Our name's Forum. I'm Myra, that's Wolf, that's Ettie and that's Wag.'

'Forum? Not Sebastian Forum's family?'

Myra was expecting that.

'Yes, he's our brother.'

'It's a mistake to be a brother of a prodigy,' said Wolfgang.

'Or a sister,' Ethel added.

The man laughed.

'I can't say you three seem to be suffering from it.' He looked at Wolfgang. 'Come on, let's have some more poetry.'

More than an hour passed during which, helped by suggestions and sometimes promptings from Myra and Ethel, Wolfgang recited almost every poem he knew. Then suddenly his inside told him the time.

'Goodness, Myra! I'm starving, it must be food time.'

Mr Oslip looked at his watch.

'Your inside is a wonderful time-keeper. It's exactly one o'clock.'

They were half-way through eating when Mr Oslip said: 'I direct films.'

'Oh!' the children answered politely, not thinking it very interesting for in America they had met lots of people connected with films. The 'Oh' sounded rather unenthusiastic so Myra added:

'Sebastian made a short in Hollywood with Misken.'

'I know,' Mr Oslip agreed. 'The film I'm going to make now is the story of an actor. He started life as a child reciter. He recited to Queen Victoria. I'm looking for a boy to play the actor as a child.' He turned to Wolfgang. 'I wonder if your father would let you act that part for me.'

For the last four years the children had got used to not making plans, so Wolfgang was resigned.

'I'm afraid not unless it's very soon. You see, we'll be gone away again by Christmas.'

'Probably to Paris for Sebastian has lessons from Dermidoff,' Ethel explained.

Mr Oslip looked thoughtful.

'December. That is a bit soon. I doubt if I'd be through with your scenes. It has to be December, has it?'

Wolfgang made a gesture with both hands.

'We expect so. It all depends on Mr Ruttenstein.'

'Everything that happens to us depends on him,' Ethel added.

Suddenly, as though he were still with her, Myra heard Grandfather's voice.

'When you decide that the time has come to have a regular home, and honestly mean it, a way will be shown you to make it happen.' The time had come and she had been shown.

'That's not true,' she said firmly. 'I mean not any more. If Wolf wants to act in your film he can, Mr Ruttenstein won't have anything to do with it.'

8

Number 10

It was lovely seeing Miss Popple again. She was waiting at the station looking more apple-ish than usual. The rest at Dan and Mary's had done her good, so she seemed more glossy and rounded. She kissed the children, patted Wag and, in her usual efficient way, in a few minutes had the luggage piled up and put on to a taxi, and before other passengers had begun to sort themselves out the family were on their way to St John's Wood.

'You're going to be very pleased with the house your father's taken,' Miss Popple said, beaming at the children as if it was a year instead of just over a month since she had seen them. 'It's old-fashioned, very English and, imagine, we've got a garden! How about that, Wag?'

There was so much news to exchange that they were nearly at the house before Myra remembered Mr Oslip.

'In the train we met a man called Mr Owen Oslip.'

'Owen Oslip!' Miss Popple sounded most impressed. 'He's

the great film man, I've read about him in my magazines from home.'

Wolfgang sounded grand.

'He asked if I could act in a film for him.'

Miss Popple's eyes looked as if they were going to jump out of her head.

'Wolfie! What an honour! Oh, dear, I wish you could, but I suppose it would take too long.'

Ethel was sitting on one of the tip-up seats; she leant forward and gave one of Miss Popple's knees an affectionate pat.

'You'll never guess what happened. Wolf and me were explaining ...'

'Wolf and I,' Miss Popple interrupted. 'Go on, dear.'

'When Myra said: "If Wolf wants to act in your film he can. Mr Ruttenstein won't have anything to do with it."'

Miss Popple gaped at Myra as if she was seeing a new person.

'My dear! Whatever made you say that?'

Again Myra could hear Grandfather's voice.

'Grandfather said it, he said that when I decided the time had come for us to have a proper home, if I honestly meant it, a way would be shown me how to have it. I think Mr Oslip is the way.'

Miss Popple, making little surprised noises, began to collect the small luggage.

'Your Grandfather said that! Well, really! Great minds think alike, I suppose. My brother Dan was on at me about the same thing. "It's time those children settled down." That's what he said.'

'And what did you say?' Wolfgang asked.

'Well, dear, at the time it sounded impossible, you know we're so used to Mr Ruttenstein's plans, but perhaps if that is what your Grandfather said we should think again.' The taxi stopped. 'Here we are. This is Number 10.'

Number 10 was as nice a house as a rented house full of other people's things could be, and the garden was wonderful for a town garden, with quite a big lawn with flower-beds all round it. But what the children liked best about the house were Mr and Mrs Bottle, who had been rented with it. They were cockneys, types the children had not before known. Both the Bottles were in the hall to greet them, Mrs Bottle, a roundabout of a woman, with a cooking apron tied round her enormous waist. Mr Bottle sandy, with a red, cheerful face.

'So this is the first shipment of Forums,' he said to Miss Popple. 'And very nice too.' Then he looked at Wag. 'But you be careful, young feller-me-lad, you won't 'alf catch it if I find you digging up my dahlias.'

Mrs Bottle grinned at Myra.

'Don't you listen to Mr B., dear, 'e wouldn't 'urt a fly. Now I must get your teas. Reckon you're starving.'

Nobody could starve in Number 10 for Mrs Bottle, who was what she called a good plain cook, believed all children ought to have enormous appetites. Because of this, when they came down to tea, the children found not only five kinds of cake, four sorts of sandwiches but fish knives and forks.

'Just a relish to keep you going,' Mrs Bottle said, slapping down a large dish of kippers in front of Miss Popple. 'There's no strength in snacks eaten on a train.'

Over tea the children told Miss Popple more about Mr Oslip.

'Mr Oslip gave Myra a card with his address, he said would Daddy or someone ring him up about me,' Wolf said.

Ethel looked sadly at Wolf.

'You'll be more awful than usual if you're a film star.' She turned to Miss Popple. 'It's about a test to see if Wolf looks right that Daddy is to phone.'

Myra made a we-understand-each-other face at Miss Popple.

'But quite honestly we didn't think Mr Oslip thought Wolf needed a test, he could see he was clever, which was no wonder for Wolf showed off dreadfully.'

Wolf looked pleased with himself.

'Absolutely true, I appreciate an audience.'

While she was unpacking before tea Miss Popple had found an idea growing in her head.

'Your Mumsdad and Mumsmum are coming round tonight. I wonder whether perhaps we should tell them, they will be sure to know how your mother will feel.'

Ethel stopped eating.

'My goodness! If Wolf does act in a film and it takes until after Christmas why couldn't we all stay? If we do I could have my audition.'

Once more it was as if Grandfather was with her prodding Myra on.

'I think you should write to Madame Leninskya anyway, Ettie. Even if you're too young for the school at this minute they could say when they would have you, and perhaps tell you who should teach you now.'

Miss Popple sounded breathless.

'Oh, dear! Such plans! But I suppose writing could do no harm. I mean, if we should be in London for some months, where you have dancing lessons will be important.'

For some months! The words hung in the air, glittering like a Christmas tree ornament.

'Eating meals at this table at the same time every day for months and months,' Wolfgang purred.

Ethel bounced joyfully on her chair.

'Just ordinary people, not world citizens.'

'Do you suppose, Popps,' Myra said in a hushed voice, for it seemed too lovely a thing to talk about out loud, 'we could stay long enough to have our own furniture out of store?'

Miss Popple felt the children were letting their dreams get out of hand.

'We mustn't count our chickens. First of all, in spite of what you felt, we must accept that Wolf may not prove suitable.'

Wolfgang swept that aside.

'Don't let that worry you. I'll be suitable all right. I could see Mr Oslip thinking I was.'

Ethel gave Miss Popple a woman-to-woman look.

'Myra was right, Popps. It's true. I don't like to think of Wolf as a film star, he'll be unbearable, but that's how Mr Oslip saw him.'

That seemed to make Miss Popple even more breathless.

'I'm sure we're being foolish. Even if you're offered the part, Wolf, we know you're very unlikely to be allowed to accept it. You know how strongly your mother feels about keeping the family together. Please, dears, you must be prepared for disappointment.'

Myra felt Grandfather's hand on her shoulder.

'Every family should have a home, a place to rest their bones, where they belong. Don't you think, Popps, perhaps Mummy would see that if we explained? I think it's just something she doesn't want because she's never thought about it.'

Miss Popple was now definitely worried. The children, particularly Myra, had changed in the last weeks. They had forgotten how wrapped up in being sure their children were lucky their father and mother were. Mr and Mrs Forum never went to films so quite likely they would only laugh and Mrs Forum would say: 'We don't want any silly old film interfering with our plans, do we, darlings?' and run off in the way she did, certain that everybody agreed with her.

'Now let's stop dreaming and finish the unpacking. We want to be shipshape by the time your grandparents arrive.'

The children had seen more of Mumsdad and Mumsmum than they had of Grandfather and Grandmother for they had come down sometimes to Apple Bough. They remembered them as town people wearing grand clothes, but as nice as Grandfather and Grandmother, only in a different way. Now that they saw them again they found they had remembered right, they were nice, and also they had a splendid unfussy way of forgetting the last four years, so they behaved as if they had seen the children yesterday. This actually was exactly how Mumsdad and Mumsmum felt, for whenever their daughter Polly stayed with them she talked about the children most of the time, and they had, of course, received photographs of them regularly.

Mumsdad was fatter than the children remembered him,

at least fatter in front just above the top of his trousers. Mumsmum looked much the same except that now she filled out her smart clothes in what Ethel called a sofa-ish way. Mumsdad, perhaps because he was something in the City, had a lets-not-waste-time way of talking.

'House all right?'

'Grand,' said Wolf. 'We've each got a bedroom to ourselves.'

Ethel hugged Mumsmum.

'There's a towel-rail in mine just right for a barre to practise my dancing.'

Mumsmum laughed.

'Be careful you don't pull it off the wall. The owners of this house are friends of mine. I don't want to hear when they come back that you pulled it to bits.'

That was so much what the children were used to hearing it made for a moment seeing Mumsmum and Mumsdad again less glorious. Mumsdad seemed to feel this.

'Don't listen to your Mumsmum. If Ettie pulls down a towel-rail I'd call it fair wear and tear. Now, let's see your dog, Myra.'

While Mumsdad was admiring Wag Myra was screwing herself up to tell about Mr Oslip. It was, she told Miss Popple afterwards, difficult to do because Grandfather seemed to have left her and gone back to Devonshire.

'We met a man on the train today, Mumsdad.'

Mumsdad was playing with Wag's ears.

'Did you now. Funny-looking little fellow, aren't you? Bit of a Heinz, but they're always the best, aren't they?' He looked up at Myra. 'What sort of man?'

Myra knew Mumsdad spent most of his spare time playing the 'cello with an amateur quartet so he probably never went to pictures, but perhaps Mumsmum did. She turned to her.

'He said he was Owen Oslip.'

Mumsdad might be more interested in Chamber music than anything else, but that name made him sit up.

'The film fellow. Fancy that! What had he got to say?'

'He asked Wolf to act in his next picture,' said Ethel.

Mumsdad had a laugh which started in his tummy before it rolled up through him. It sounded like the sea swirling over shingle. He gave one of his laughs now.

'What grandchildren I've got! My grandson, Sebastian, becomes internationally famous at eight. Now my other grandson is asked to act in a film by the great Owen Oslip. And what did you say, Wolfie?'

'I didn't,' Wolfgang explained. 'It was Myra who did. I thought I couldn't because Sebastian's last concert being early December Mr Ruttenstein had fixed for us to go back to Paris. But Myra said if I wanted to act in the film I could, it wouldn't be anything to do with Mr Ruttenstein.'

'And Myra was quite right,' Mumsmum agreed, 'for if you're needed here after the others go to Paris you can stay with us.'

Before she had time to bite it back a miserable 'Oh, no!' slipped out of Myra's mouth. Both Mumsdad and Mumsmum looked at her.

'Why "Oh, no"?' Mumsdad asked.

Though she did not want to because she did not know yet who they would side with, Myra tried to explain.

'It's not we don't like being all together, of course we do, actually we hate Daddy, Mummy and Sebastian being away.'

Ethel thought Myra was explaining in a muddly way.

'Being a world citizen for ever and ever can get wearing.'

'And learning geography from travel instead of atlases like ordinary children isn't all it's cracked up to be,' Wolfgang added.

'We didn't sort of know how we felt all at once,' Myra went on, 'it kind of crept up on us how dreadfully we want a home, with our own furniture in it. Then in Devonshire Grandfather told me, if I wanted a home badly enough, I'd be shown a way to get it.'

Wolfgang, who was sitting on the arm of Mumsmum's armchair, gave her shoulder a prod.

'Grandfather told us that bit of the Bible about talents and the idiot who buried his. He told about the Bible because he's a clergyman.'

Ethel, sitting on a stool at Mumsmum's feet, was bouncing with eagerness to speak.

'What we think he meant was even if your talent is awful, like Wolf's for writing pop music.'

'That's a nasty bit of news,' Mumsdad murmured.

'He ought to slave at it, like I ought at my dancing.'

Myra looked anxiously at Mumsdad to see if he was understanding.

'He thought it was time we thought about our talents and not just Sebastian's, and we can't do that while we travel wherever Sebastian goes.'

Wolfgang prodded Mumsmum again.

'Like a tail follows a dog.'

'Then on a walk,' Myra went on, 'Grandfather said that thing about being shown a way to get a home, and I hoped Mr Oslip was the way. But if you tell Daddy and Mummy Wolf can stay with you we haven't a hope.'

Over the children's heads Mumsdad and Mumsmum exchanged a look. The children saw the look but did not know what it meant. Then Mumsdad said:

'So that's what you want. Funny, your Mumsmum and I have been worried. We never saw you – and your mother, as you know, thinks you're the luckiest children alive to be living the way you do.'

Mumsmum nodded.

'But we wondered. Only last time your mother stayed with us I said: "Are you sure the children like all this travelling?" but I had to believe her when she said you adored it.'

'Abhorred it would explain better,' said Wolfgang.

Ethel was bouncing again.

'It's Mr Ruttenstein. To him we're just part of Sebastian, like his luggage.'

Myra was afraid they were sounding disloyal.

'We'd simply hate it if Daddy and Mummy were away and we were here, but we – or, anyway, I – thought perhaps, if something happened which kept us here quite a long time, Mummy would feel how nice it was to stay in one place. I thought this film might be the thing to make that happen.'

Mumsmum again gave Mumsdad a look, but this time it was clear that it meant Myra could be right. Mumsdad turned to Wolfgang.

'Have you this fellow Oslip's address?'

Wolfgang slid off the arm of Mumsmum's chair.

'It's on a card, I'll get it.'

While Wolfgang was away Mumsdad beckoned to Myra.

'Come here, Granddaughter.'

Followed by Wag Myra, wondering what he wanted, came to him and stood facing him. He took her hands. 'You think you've explained badly, don't you?'

She nodded.

'Nobody loves their father and mother more than we love ours.'

Mumsdad smiled in a very fond way.

'You've made that clear, in fact you've made everything clear. I think you're probably right, and if this film turns up for Wolfie it could mean a stop to this roaring round the earth. It would be fun, wouldn't it, if tonight we saw the beginning of what I shall call "Operation Home"?'

9

Plans

Mumsdad was a person who, having decided to do something, wasted no time in getting it done. So the very next day he called in at Number 10 on his way back from the City. It was a wet evening and he found the children in the room which was going to be the schoolroom. Myra was knitting a winter pullover for Wag, Wolfgang was picking out a new tune on the piano, interrupted by Ethel, who complained of the lack of beat for she was trying to dance to it, but they all dropped what they were doing to rush to Mumsdad.

'I find it most satisfactory to be in a place where relations can just walk in,' said Wolfgang.

Ethel pulled Mumsdad towards the only armchair.

'Just like happens to ordinary children.'

As Mumsdad sat, Myra perched on the arm of his chair.

'Can we come and visit you and Mumsmum after church on Sundays? That, we've noticed, is what proper families do.'

Mumsdad, in a way which they were beginning to realise

was special to him, wasted no time answering questions that had nothing to do with the business he had come about.

'Your Mr Oslip lunched with me today, Wolfie. He said he definitely wants you for this film. However, there is to be a test so I told him I would like to get the preliminaries fixed before your parents get home. You are to go to the studio tomorrow.' He turned to Myra. 'You and Ettie are expected too. It seems a lunch is owing.'

'That's perfectly right,' Ethel agreed. 'We gave him some of ours on the train.'

'Grandmother's marvellous at picnic food,' Myra explained.

'And packs tons,' Wolfgang added. 'We'd enough for three more Mr Oslips.'

Mumsdad, as if they had not spoken, went on with what he had come to say.

'We discussed your contract, Wolfie.'

Wolfgang, who was not normally a boy who was ever calm had, up to that moment, taken the fact he might act in a film calmly, but now at the word 'contract' he became impressed with himself.

'A contract! Me with a contract! A real proper one like Sebastian has?'

Mumsdad nodded.

'Every bit as proper and twice as long I shouldn't wonder, for there's a lot to arrange. A car has to take you to and from the film studio, and the studio is supposed to provide a governess or tutor, who will also act as chaperon, but in your case it will be Miss Popple, I suppose.'

Myra felt Mumsdad was so good at arranging things, he might imagine a governess for Wolf was something that could be settled in a minute, while she knew it could not, so she laid a restraining hand on his arm.

'Popps teaches all of us so she couldn't be spared just for Wolf, and Mummy would never let him go to a film studio with a strange person. I know she wouldn't.'

Mumsdad was like a steam-roller, he flattened out troubles.

'There will be a way round that problem.' He looked at Ethel, who was holding on to the table while she did a plié. 'If you can spare time from your practice, Ettie, come here for I've some news for you too.' Ethel came to him and stood between his knees. He put an arm round her. 'I talked on the telephone to your Madame Leninskya this afternoon.'

Ethel was shocked.

'Without saying you were going to? She wouldn't have liked that. You might have interrupted a class.'

'Don't worry. I was most respectful, and all in French, which is an easier language to be respectful in than English.' He looked in a pleased way at Ethel. 'It seems yet another of my grandchildren may be on the road to success. Did you ever hear of a Madame Fidolia?'

Ethel clasped her hands, her eyes sparkling like birthday candles.

'Have I? Of course I have. Posy Fossil learnt at her school until she went to Manoff, and she's the greatest dancer in the world.'

'Well, your Madame Leninskya thinks that you should go there for at least a year before your audition for The Royal Ballet School. Madame Fidolia's school – what a lot of Madames – is an all-day affair, you do your lessons there and are taught to act as well as to dance. I arranged that

Madame Leninskya would telephone to Madame Fidolia about you, French posts are so slow.'

Myra felt out of breath, Mumsdad was making plans so fast.

'You're the quickest arranger I ever met.'

'Have to be if Operation Home is to get going.' Then Mumsdad lowered his voice as though he was making them part of a secret society. 'I am sure the great thing is for us to get all preliminary plans made before your father and mother get home. We know your mother doesn't like making arrangements, she hated making them even when she was a little girl, and she hasn't changed, but when some-one else makes them it's been my experience she usually falls in with them without a murmur.'

'That's why she's so fond of Mr Ruttenstein,' Wolfgang agreed. 'I shouldn't think there's ever been in the whole world someone who was so good at making plans for other people as him.'

But Myra was still worried.

'We know Mummy hates making plans, which is why she likes someone like Mr Ruttenstein to make them for her, but his are plans for all of us, our plans are for splitting us up.'

Mumsdad patted the leg of Myra's which was near-est to him.

'You never win anything worth having without taking risks. My idea of Operation Home is that it should include you all. Did you know Queen Victoria had a granddaugh-ter called Princess Ena?' Myra shook her head. 'Well, she had – she was about your age when the boy reciter came to Windsor, so she was allowed to hear him, at least in the film she hears him. Now I had told Mr Oslip about Miss Popple – that there might be a snag there – so he said why couldn't you play the Princess, then you would have to go to the studio, which would mean you and Wolf could share Miss Popple.'

Myra felt as if she were Alice falling down the rabbit hole, but before she could say anything Wolfgang did.

'That's a simply terrible idea! Myra couldn't act.'

Ethel agreed with him.

'Not the littlest, tiniest bit, and she'd simply hate it, so that idea's out.'

Mumsdad refused to be put off.

'Princess Ena doesn't say a word. She's just audience. You wouldn't mind that, would you, Myra? It makes the arrangements for lessons sound easy, and I'm sure the easier they sound the more likely it is that your mother will fall in with them.'

'Well, that would settle me and Wolf,' Myra agreed, 'and Ettie too if she goes to Madame Fidolia's school. But what about Sebastian?'

Mumsdad nodded.

'I haven't forgotten him, but we can only move one step at a time, so we'll tackle the Sebastian problem when he's back. The question now is, will you help by being the Princess?'

Though the mere thought of acting in a film made Myra feel as if she had swallowed a lump of ice cream much too fast, just being in one without saying anything was not much to give in return for being shown a way to have what Grandfather had called a 'regular home'.

'I won't be any good even as audience. But if it's my way to help I'll do it.'

Mumsdad got up.

'That's my girl. Now I must talk to Miss Popple about arrangements for tomorrow.'

After the children were in bed Miss Popple told the Bottles about tomorrow's plans.

'Breakfast will have to be sharp at eight, Mrs Bottle, the studio car is coming for us at nine.'

Mr and Mrs Bottle had been watching television but Mr Bottle turned it off.

'Wasn't worth seeing,' he said, as Miss Popple looked apologetic. 'Comics get less comic every day. Mrs Bottle and me was talkin' about this film lark over tea. Take it very calm, don't they?'

Miss Popple sat down.

'It must seem like that to you, I suppose. You see, being Sebastian's sisters and brother they've always been invited everywhere. They've been to studios in Hollywood several times.'

Mrs Bottle had heavy corsets with bones to hold in her fat. They creaked when she moved. They creaked now.

'Young Wolf's so confident like. "Oh, I'll get the part," he says, just as I might say I'd buy a pound of sugar. "You watch out," I says, "pride comes before a fall."'

Miss Popple struggled to explain.

'It's not really pride. Mind you, I'm not saying that Wolfie is not conceited for, in a way, he is, but it's more that he's confident. He does recite nicely and, in the Forums' world of artists, pretending you don't do something well when you do, is considered affectation.'

'But young Myra isn't like that,' Mr Bottle said. '"I 'ave

to be a Princess, Mr Bottle," she says, "I don't say anything but even doing nothin' I'll be terrible."'

Miss Popple knew the Bottles were getting fond of the children and that was why they wanted to understand.

'But that's true too, Myra is a charming child but she has no talent and she admits it, but you try asking Ettie about her dancing and you'll find she's just as confident in her own way as Wolfie is in his.'

Mrs Bottle got up.

'We were just goin' to 'ave a cuppa, you'll 'ave one, won't you, dear?' She filled the kettle before she creaked back into her chair. 'You see, we'd six of our own – all married now – and we taught 'em to keep quiet about what they were doin'.'

'That's right,' Mr Bottle broke in. '"All right, all right," I'd say, "is your trumpeter dead that you've got to bray like a donkey about yourselves!"'

Miss Popple laughed.

'Certainly Wolfie is his own trumpeter, and up to a point so is Ettie, and really I'm glad. You see, living as they have under the shadow of Sebastian, who everybody says is brilliant – I wouldn't know because I can't hear music – the other children might so easily have had no self-confidence, for they've always been treated merely as Sebastian's relations.'

'Left its mark on young Myra, I'd say,' said Mrs Bottle. 'Old 'ead on young shoulders, she 'as.'

'And you're quite right,' Miss Popple agreed.

'Proper old-fashioned, she is.' Then Mrs Bottle beamed at Miss Popple. 'Don't you worry, dear, Bottle and me 'ave taken to the children, and if they seem peculiar like in some ways we'll get used to 'em.'

The test, as Wolfgang had supposed, did not bother him a bit. He had to recite 'O to be in England'. Then there was a scene where he came for his reciting lesson to find his elocution master dead. For this Wolfgang had to open a door, walk into a room, say 'Good-morning, sir,' then see the man lying on his bed. Go up to him. Then shrink back and say, 'He's dead! He's dead!'

'This is the story of a real actor, Wolf,' Mr Oslip said, 'so this really happened to him. He was only eight and he was so frightened he never forgot it.'

'I can imagine it would upset a child of that age,' Wolfgang agreed.

'Well, I want you to feel eight and so scared you're never going to forget it.'

The first time Wolfgang tried to act that scene he was very funny. Not feeling scared he did what he thought a little boy of eight might do. He opened his eyes until they were round as saucers, then he staggered backwards screaming, 'He's dead! He's dead!'

Mr Oslip, though he laughed, was having none of that sort of nonsense.

'Very funny,' he said, 'but now let's see what really happened.' Then he had a whispered conversation with the actor who was standing – or rather lying – in for the elocution master. As a result, the next time Wolfgang did the scene he had put on some make-up and looked so dead that Wolfgang really was scared, and looked it, and said in just the right kind of whisper, 'He's dead!' Mr Oslip was pleased.

The last test was reciting before Queen Victoria. For this, as well as having an actress who pretended to be Queen

Victoria, Mr Oslip put Myra to sit at her feet as Princess Ena, but so that Myra wouldn't feel shy, he asked Ethel to be there too.

'This time you only have to bow and look shy and polite,' Mr Oslip explained to Wolfgang.

That made Ethel laugh.

'I like that "only". Wolf's never felt shy in his life.'

Mr Oslip said he quite believed it. But even Wolfgang might have felt a little shy if he was meeting Queen Victoria.

Evidently Wolfgang's face looked all right for quite soon Mr Oslip said 'cut' and the test was over and now they could have lunch. But before they went to it he put an arm round Myra.

'You'll look fine. That wasn't so bad, was it?'

'No,' Myra agreed, 'but that was only a test. I'll be scared stiff when it's the real picture.'

'Not you,' said Mr Oslip. 'It'll be fun, and remember, you'll be dressed for the part. That's always a great help.'

Mr Oslip's lunch was perfect. Just the sort of food the children and Miss Popple liked. There was a steak and kidney pudding with blackberry tart and cream to follow, and at the end of it he gave each of them a box of chocolates, and he sent a bone tied with a scarlet bow home to Wag.

'We'll be starting work somewhere in October,' he told them as he said goodbye. 'And, by the way, Miss Popple, Wolfgang is not to have his hair cut. I hate wigs so he can use his own hair but it must be long. You see, for reciting in public he wears a Lord Fauntleroy suit.'

That evening both Mumsmum and Mumsdad came round to find out how Wolfgang had got on, so Wolfgang who, since the audition, had been what Miss Popple called 'thoroughly above himself', went through the whole test for both of them and for Mr and Mrs Bottle, using Mr Bottle for the unconscious man. Mumsmum and Mumsdad were amused, but Mrs Bottle was a wonderful audience.

'Oh, come off it, Wolfie,' she said, when rather overdoing it Wolfgang said, 'He's dead!' as he leant over Mr Bottle. 'Proper turned me over, you did. I don't want to lose my old man yet.'

Having started to arrange things there seemed no stopping Mumsdad. For after hearing all about the day at the studio, he said:

'And there's another busy day for you all tomorrow, only this time with Ettie as star. Madame Fidolia is expecting her at eleven.'

Madame Fidolia's school was called The Children's Academy of Dancing and Stage Training. It was in Bloomsbury and was three houses converted into one. There were a lot of new buildings round it, and beside them the Academy looked shabby, but the children thought this proper for most of the music and dancing schools they had known abroad were in need of doing up.

The door was opened by a pupil. She was about fifteen and was wearing what she explained was the ordinary school uniform, a black overall with a little high collar such as the children had seen worn in Russia. On her left side she wore a badge with a big P on it. She said this stood for prefect and that amongst a prefect's duties in the holidays when there was no school was answering the door.

'Madame said I was to take you straight to her office,' the

girl said to Ethel. 'You'll be able to change your shoes in the dance classroom.'

Ethel had a horror of dancing in the wrong clothes, so she was wearing her practice tunic under a coat. She had her shoes in a bag. Myra marvelled at how calm she looked. If it was me, she thought, I'd be fainting with fright.

Ethel was anything but fainting with fright. As she was the one concerned she stepped forward to join the girl to lead the way to Madame's office.

'Do we do dancing every day?' she asked.

The girl nodded.

'Of some sort. Ballet is every afternoon, but some mornings it's tap and others it's character.'

Ethel was surprised.

'Tap and character! I wouldn't have thought a friend of Madame Leninskya would teach those.'

The girl looked squashing.

'I don't know Madame Leninskya but we all do tap and character here. We shouldn't get any panto work without. We all do it, that is except the specials. They do extra ballet instead.'

'That's what I'll do,' said Ethel.

The girl looked down at her.

'How old are you?'

'Nine.'

'Nobody counts much in this school until they're twelve, and old enough to have a licence. If you come here I wouldn't throw your weight about, it won't go down well with the juniors.'

They all heard this. Myra was just about to say that Ethel

never threw her weight about when Wolfgang dashed to the rescue.

'It's affected to pretend you can't do something well when you can, didn't anyone ever tell you that?'

Miss Popple was fussed. She knew Ethel was not meaning to be vain, but it would not help her in the school if she arrived with a reputation for conceit.

'She's quite right, Ettie, it's silly for a little girl of your age to say what you'll learn and won't learn before you've even been accepted as a pupil.'

They had reached Madame Fidolia's room. The girl knocked, but before they went in Ethel gave Miss Popple a wink.

'Madame Fidolia'll accept me all right.'

Madame Fidolia was an old lady, but she was still very much head of her school though nowadays she left the day-to-day running of it to younger women. But she still taught ballet and had just come from a class when the children and Miss Popple came in. Many of the musicians and painters the children had met were odd to look at, and so had many of Ethel's dancing teachers been, including Madame Leninskya, so to them Madame Fidolia did not look noticeably queer, though to many people she did look strange. Old though she was she still had jet black hair, parted in the middle and drawn down into a bun on her neck. She was wearing a black taffeta dress with short sleeves and a full skirt with, underneath it, pink tights. On her feet were pink ballet shoes. Round her shoulders was a huge jade green shawl. She was sitting but beside her was a long black stick with a silver top, so the children guessed she was lame. She looked at each of them in turn, then fixed her attention on Ethel. She spoke with a foreign accent.

'You are Ettie?'

Ethel swept down in one of Madame Leninskya's curtsies.

'Yes, Madame.'

Madame Fidolia looked approving.

'Very nice. Leninskya still expects curtsies. So do I.' She smiled at Myra. 'Do you not wish to come here too, my child?'

Myra gave a quick bob.

'No, thank you. I'm no earthly good at dancing.'

'Dancing is not all we teach, in fact very few of my pupils hope to be dancers. They learn how to act here.'

'I can't do that either,' Myra explained.

Madame turned her dark eyes to Wolfgang.

'It is you who is to act in a film, yes?'

Wolfgang gave a nice bow.

'That's right, but I don't mean to be an actor when I grow up. I mean to compose songs.'

Madame Fidolia got up and, helped by her stick, led the way to the door.

'I trust you may get your wish. Now we must go to my classroom for I must see what you have learnt, Ettie, before I place you.'

In the main dancing-room about forty boys and girls, all dressed alike in blue shorts and shirts, were learning tap dancing. A very energetic girl called Miss Carrot was teaching them. At the piano a fat lady wearing a smart hat was playing for the class, reading a newspaper at the same time. The children, used to piano playing treated with respect, were amazed. Wolfgang was so surprised he had to go to the piano to see if his eyes had seen properly.

'It was really happening,' he told the others on the way home, 'and that tap-dancing music you would think needed concentration, with that heavily marked beat. But not her, she just went on thump, thump, thump and read what the furniture's like where Princess Margaret lives, for I looked over her shoulder and saw.'

The routine the children were learning came to an end. Madame Fidolia beckoned to Miss Carrot who, before she spoke, dropped a deep, respectful curtsy.

'Madame.'

Madame Fidolia made a gesture towards Ethel, who was changing her shoes.

'That is Ettie Forum who has been sent to me by my old friend Madame Leninskya. I would like to see her work.'

'Right,' said the teacher. Then, in a voice which echoed round the room, she shouted 'Sit.' In a second the whole class was sitting cross-legged on the floor.

Madame Fidolia pointed in a grand way to a bench.

'You may sit there,' she said to Miss Popple.

As quickly and inconspicuously as possible Myra and Miss Popple sat.

'She couldn't be grander if this was Windsor Castle,' Miss Popple whispered.

But Myra was thinking of Ethel.

'How awful for Ettie with all those children watching.'

Ethel could not have cared less how many children were in the room. Looking very nice in her white tunic she went quietly to the barre in the centre of the wall and waited to be told what to do. For five minutes Madame rapped out orders, such as 'Demi-plié in fourth.' 'Grand battement.' 'Arabesque.' 'Frappés.' Then she told Ethel she would now see what she could do in the centre. There she made her spin across the room in a series of pirouettes. Then she said she would like to see her elevation, so she asked for several jumps, and finally she asked for a series of steps and jumps, finishing with an arabesque. Then she said she would like to look at Ethel's feet.

Ethel was wearing socks so she sat down on the floor and took them and her shoes off. Madame Fidolia walked round her, looking at her legs and feet, just as Myra had seen men who owned restaurants look at meat in butchers' shops in Paris. Then she called Miss Carrot over to look too.

'You should study these feet, Miss Carrot, for they are true dancer's feet.' Then she patted Ethel on the shoulder. 'You have been well taught but there are weaknesses. You will be in my special ballet class. You will as well learn character dancing from Miss Carrot. You will not learn tap. You are dismissed.'

In spite of having bare feet, which are not perfect for the job, Ethel swept another beautiful curtsy.

'Thank you, Madame.'

As Madame Fidolia passed the bench where they were sitting, Miss Popple and Myra sprang to their feet and Myra gave a little bob.

'What did you do that for?' Wolfgang asked when they got outside. 'She never saw you, she was only thinking of Ettie.'

'I didn't exactly do it,' Myra tried to explain. 'My legs did it without asking me. Madame Fidolia's that sort of person.'

'She is indeed,' Miss Popple agreed. 'I had no idea I was standing up until I found I was, and I'm sure if I saw her often I'd start to curtsy.'

Ethel shamed them by dancing all the way home, even on the platform of the Underground.

'I do wish you wouldn't,' Myra begged: 'in England people don't.'

'I don't care what English people don't do,' said Ethel. 'I feel like dancing so I shall dance.'

10

Sebastian Comes Home

The family came home. Mumsdad went to meet them at the airport so that he could break the news of the plans to Polly before she reached Number 10. He was lucky, there were a lot of camera men and reporters to meet Sebastian so he suggested driving Polly home, leaving David to deal with them.

At first Polly, who was thrilled to be with her father, did all the talking. She told him about Misken's concerto, what the Press had said about it and what they had said about Sebastian's playing of it. The people they had met and the great musical reception after the Misken concert. Presently Mumsdad stopped her.

'Wonderful, darling. I'm longing to read the press cuttings. But now I want to talk to you about the other three.'

All the gaiety went out of Polly's face.

'You said they were all right. It's the first thing I asked.'

Mumsdad was holding one of her hands, now he gave it a pat.

'So they are, very much all right. But they, too, have been having excitements. Wolfie is acting in a film.'

'Wolf! But he's only a baby. How did he get a part in a film?'

Mumsdad shook his head at her.

'What nonsense! He's eleven. Sebastian had an international reputation, if I remember rightly, when he was eight.'

Polly made a face at him.

'Don't niggle. Sebastian's different. How can Wolfie make a film? We can't all go to the studio every day and I'm certainly not allowing him to go alone.'

Mumsdad knew his daughter. He talked in his most leave-it-to-me voice.

'As soon as I heard about the film – that fellow Oslip's making it, by the way.'

'Oslip!' Polly might not go to a film often but she knew that name. 'However did he find Wolfie?'

'On the train. Let him tell you. I knew you wouldn't let him go alone so I've fixed a small silent part for Myra. That means Miss Popple can take them both.'

'Myra! In a film! But, darling Dad, Myra couldn't act if the alternative was being burnt at the stake.'

'Doesn't have to. Just sits at Queen Victoria's feet. She's a Princess.'

'But if Myra and Wolfie have Miss Popple, what about Sebastian and Ettie?'

'Ettie's fixed. You know that Leninskya woman you sent her to in Paris?' Polly nodded. 'Well, she wants her to go to a Madame Fidolia while she's here. Madame F. has a proper school, lessons and all.'

Polly looked horrified.

'Poor little Ettie. Why should she be pushed off to a school?'

'You try and stop her going. You can be tough, darling, but I'd back Ettie.'

Polly did not like all these plans. She tried to pull her hand away from her father's.

'You're a meddling old man. What's the good of Ettie going to a school for a couple of months? It's to get around the difficulty that we're always moving that we have a governess.'

Mumsdad was expecting that and avoided arguing. Instead he said:

'They're fine children, Polly.'

'Of course they're fine. I told you they were. But you can't soft soap me. What about Sebastian? Where have you planned he does his lessons while his home is broken up because Myra and Wolfie are at a film studio, and Ettie at a school?'

Mumsdad could not help laughing.

'You sound as if your family were going to the ends of the earth. But they will in actual fact all be home each evening. As for Sebastian, I think you would have found he would have had to have had his own tutor while he's here in any case. Remember how small the island is; even you could not want to cart the whole family, plus Miss Popple, to places like Birmingham and Bath, from which he can get back, if not on the same evening the next day.'

Polly knew her father was talking sense but she still had to argue.

'The children have always done everything together.'

Mumsdad felt she was weakening.

'So they still will. What a fuss to make about a bit of filming and some dancing classes.'

Put that way it did seem foolish to be in a state. And anyway, what a day to get in a state, Polly thought, when in a short time she would have all her family under one roof.

'All right. I'm a grumbling Mum. But we have always had such fun travelling together and doing things together. I hate plans to spoil things, even for a few months.'

When they got to Number 10 Mumsdad managed to talk to Myra alone.

'I've told your mother all our plans, but I kept off how long Wolfie's film might last. I know you won't say anything but do warn Wolfie and Ettie to be careful. If the film lasting into next year comes up now I think your mother might tear up Wolfie's contract. She must get used to the idea slowly.'

It was not easy to get Wolfgang and Ethel on their own, for not only had they to show Polly every inch of the house and garden, but there were the Bottles to introduce, and there were frequent rushes to the front gate to see if there was any sign of David and Sebastian. At last Polly was tired and said she must put on some trousers as she felt a stuffed shirt in her travelling clothes. That was Myra's chance; she beckoned Wolfgang and Ethel into the schoolroom and in a whisper told them what Mumsdad had said.

'What sort of fool does Mumsdad think I am?' Wolfgang asked indignantly. 'He's told us and told us not to say anything about Operation Home. I don't need telling again.'

'Nor me,' Ethel agreed. 'But I'm glad Mumsdad has told Mummy I'm going to Madame Fidolia's school. I was bursting to tell her but I thought I better wait.'

David and Sebastian did not arrive until nearly suppertime. Sebastian, Myra thought, not only looked tired but somehow smaller all over than before he went to Hollywood. But she had no chance then to talk to him, for Mumsmum and Mumsdad were there, and everybody was so anxious to tell their own news they had no time to listen to other people's, in fact, at first they all talked at once.

Mrs Bottle had excelled herself cooking a superb welcome-home supper. There was the children's favourite soup made of potato, roast chicken with masses of bread sauce, jellies served in orange skins with angelica handles, so that they looked like baskets, and a tremendous trifle covered in whipped cream, nuts and cherries, just the sort of trifle Miss Popple had tried to teach cooks all over the world to make but had never quite succeeded. With this the grown-ups drank champagne and the children Coca-Cola. At the end of supper Mumsdad raised his glass and cleared his throat in a I'm-going-to-make-a-speech way.

'This is a very great evening, my dear Polly and David. You can't know what it means to us to have you all home at last.' Then he looked at Sebastian. 'Here's to your success, Sebastian, in your native land.'

Then David got up and raised his glass.

'I gather Sebastian's not the only one whose health we have to drink. Here's to your film, Wolfie.'

Before they had finished drinking to that Ethel was bouncing on her chair to attract attention.

'Isn't anybody going to drink my health? I'm the person Madame Fidolia said had true dancer's feet.'

'It's time those dancer's feet were in bed,' said Miss Popple.

So after Ethel's health had been drunk she went upstairs and soon afterwards Wolfgang followed. Then Mrs Bottle came in to say coffee was in the living-room and the grown-ups went off to drink it, so that left Myra and Sebastian sitting alone over the remains of the party.

'I know what the press cuttings say, but how was the concerto truly?' Myra asked.

Sebastian was playing with the orange skin on his plate.

'Almost perfect, but I didn't like the rehearsals much.'

'Why?'

Sebastian took a knife and began cutting a tooth edge round the orange skin.

'Misken wanted to hear his concerto most days, so a man called Raccochi conducted for him. He's been appointed a deputy conductor there.'

'You didn't like his conducting?'

'No. Nor did Misken.' A smile turned up the corners of Sebastian's mouth. 'He called him Mr Bear. He said he conducted like a bear in a zoo asking for buns.'

Myra cleared a space to put her arms on the table so she could rest her chin on them, which was a favourite position of hers for listening.

'You mean the way they wave both paws?'

'Yes. You know how Misken uses his left hand as if it was a separate person talking, well Raccochi only uses his left hand to imitate his right – it says nothing. That made rehearsals hard.'

They were silent a moment while Myra thought about conducting. Could bad rehearsals be the reason Sebastian looked smaller all over? She decided there was something more.

'Was everything else all right?'

This time the pause was because Sebastian found it hard to explain what he felt.

'It was different without all of you. You know how it is after a concert. When I go home with you, if it isn't late, we do something ordinary.'

'Like Snap or Spillikins,' Myra agreed.

Sebastian stopped cutting his orange-skin to look at her.

'It was awful, Myra. Daddy and Mummy didn't stay long at places after rehearsals, I mean, not longer than they could help, but of course I had to go too.'

Myra could picture that, so she knew why Sebastian looked shrunk. After a rehearsal or a performance it was as if he had been poured away, there was no Sebastian left. It was only when there had been a lot of laughing and silly family jokes, and perhaps they had played a game, that he came back and could eat his supper and go to sleep.

'My goodness! Did you stay awake all night afterwards?'

'Not the whole night, but I kept waking up with a jump, as if I was falling off a cliff.'

'Was it cocktail parties?'

'Mostly. I tried sitting in a chair in the hall when there was one, but mostly at those sort of parties in Hollywood they use the hall.' Sebastian shivered as he remembered. 'People came and talked and talked.'

'About playing the fiddle, I suppose?'

'On and on,' Sebastian agreed.

'Never mind, you're here now,' Myra comforted. 'You'll come back here after concerts.'

Sebastian stared at Myra. He looked miserable.

'Will I? If Wolf is making a film, and you're in it too, and Ettie's at her dancing-school, only Daddy and Mummy will go to the towns like Manchester with me.'

Myra felt mean. Here they had been making plans, and none of them had thought how Sebastian would feel. It was hard to tell him what they were thinking, but she felt he ought to know.

'It started in Devonshire. Grandfather sort of said it was time we stopped travelling. Had a home.'

'Like this?'

'No, a real one, with our own furniture out of store.'

'Apple Bough?'

As he spoke, it was as if Apple Bough was there. For a moment it was so close Myra felt she could walk in through the gate. Then she wriggled her shoulders to push it away.

'Apple Bough would be perfect, of course, but that's only a fairy-tale idea, anyway, it was sold. But perhaps some day a house like this, only ours, with our things in it, not other people's ... '

Sebastian's eyes glowed.

'Where we could go every Rest Period?'

Myra hated to spoil Sebastian's first day home, but he had to know some time.

'Where you would come every Rest Period and the rest of us might be most of the time.' Sebastian's eyes grew as large as saucers, like the dog in the fairy story. Myra hurried on. 'Perhaps, if we had a regular home, Mr Ruttenstein could make your tours shorter.'

As she said that Sebastian, the boy who was just twelve, went away and Sebastian, the musician, took his place.

'After the concert at the party for Misken, Mr Ruttenstein said that perhaps next year, or, anyway, the year after, he would give me his violin.'

Although Myra could not play a fiddle, of course she had learnt a great deal about them just by hearing Sebastian and her father and mother talk. There are some famous violins in the world, and one of them belonged to Mr Ruttenstein.

'The Amati?'

As if it was too holy to be spoken of out loud Sebastian whispered:

'Yes.'

'Goodness!'

'It sings,' Sebastian went on in the same awed whisper. 'I must have it, Myra.'

'And you don't think Mr Ruttenstein will give it to you unless you do the tours he says you are to do?'

'I don't think so.'

Myra pressed her chin deep into her folded arms.

'Do you think he minds where you spend Rest Periods?'

Sebastian went back to cutting his orange skin.

'I don't suppose so. Except that he thinks my lessons should be from Dermidoff when I'm not with Misken. But that's only because Daddy says it's best. I think if Daddy said there was someone here I should learn with and Misken approved – then he wouldn't mind.'

Myra sat up with such a jump that she woke Wag, who was sleeping off a heavy supper under her chair.

'Work for that. Don't think of the tours, just think of the glory of Rest Periods in your really truly home. Imagine leaving things in a drawer and finding them there when you came back.'

'That would be superb,' Sebastian agreed. 'But I don't know what Mr Ruttenstein would think, and I can't risk losing the Amati, you must see that.'

Myra patted Wag, who had put his paws in her lap.

'Oh, I do. I only mean try.'

Sebastian got up.

'Touring will be awful if you aren't there.'

'You don't know yet we won't be there. Mumsdad says first things first and the first thing for all of us is a regular home, where we belong – which is England.'

Before Sebastian could answer Mrs Bottle looked round the door.

'Your Mum says it's time you were in bed, Sebastian. You goin' to lend me a 'and, young Myra? The best party 'as to come to an end sometimes, and where it ends is in me kitchen sink.'

Busy Days

Luckily for the children's plans Polly was invited to show her pictures in a London gallery. This kept her so busy she had to leave family arrangements to David and Miss Popple, so without a lot of talking about it they found a tutor for Sebastian, though really Myra had quite a lot to do with the choosing.

Sebastian's first concert was in two weeks' time, so rehearsals were starting almost at once. But because they were in England before the rehearsals started David had to take Sebastian to County Hall to get a licence to appear before a paying audience. On the morning that they were going to County Hall Miss Popple came down to breakfast looking green.

'Oh, dear, I've hardly slept a wink,' she said. 'Every time I dropped off I had a nightmare in which somebody at County Hall was saying: "Sebastian can't have a licence because he's totally uneducated."'

That made David laugh.

'That would be a nice thing with all these concerts fixed, I don't know what poor Mr Ruttenstein would say. But I don't think you need worry.'

David was quite right, there was no need for Miss Popple to worry, for Sebastian was able to satisfy the man who asked him questions that he was above standard in his school work. But he did not come off so well in his medical examination.

The doctor knew all about Sebastian, so took an especial interest in him.

'He's perfectly sound,' he told David, 'but he's thin and undersized.'

David explained all his children were small for their ages.

'My eldest, Myra, who is thirteen, doesn't look a day more than eleven.'

'There are families like that,' the doctor agreed, 'but keep an eye on this one. Spare him when you can.'

As Polly was out David went straight to the schoolroom to tell Miss Popple about County Hall. Morning lessons were over so Wolfgang and Ethel had gone out to play in the garden, but Myra was there helping to put the lesson books away.

'Sebastian came through with flying colours from the lessons' point of view.'

'Thank goodness,' said Miss Popple. 'Such a relief! Silly, I know, but I could not help worrying.'

'The doctor wasn't so pleased. He said he was undersized. I explained they all were, but I think he thought he might be doing too much, he said I should spare him when I could. He doesn't know Sebastian, I'd get my ears pinned back if I tried to cut down his practice time, or shorten his rehearsals.'

Miss Popple knew nothing about Sebastian's rehearsals, but she did know how many hours he practised and she thought it was far too many.

'I wish he'd practise less, it would be much better for him to be out of doors.'

David was devoted to Miss Popple, but she was a joke when it came to anything to do with music.

'I couldn't stop Sebastian doing the practice he thinks he needs, and I wouldn't try, but perhaps he could break it up more and while the weather lasts get out into the garden for breathers.'

Myra was standing on a stool piling books into a cupboard. But when David said that she scrambled down.

'I know how Sebastian could be spared.'

David held out a hand to her.

'Do you, old lady? How?'

Myra came to him.

'That tutor you're getting him for when we're at the studio. If you could find someone rather silly that would help.'

'But, dear,' said Miss Popple, 'he is to teach Sebastian, and somebody silly couldn't do that.'

Myra knew her father would understand.

'I don't mean that sort of silly. I mean someone who when they aren't teaching likes doing silly things. Sebastian needs that after concerts.'

David did understand.

'You think he didn't like the parties we took him to in Los Angeles? We never stayed long.'

Myra spoke firmly.

'Sebastian isn't a party sort of boy. After concerts we have to be silly for ages until the concert's worn off. If we aren't there the tutor will have to be silly instead of us.'

David looked at Miss Popple.

'There's wisdom for you!' Then he kissed Myra. 'Thank you, darling, I'll advertise for a pleasant young man who, though able to teach, is also able to play.'

So that was how Paul Ingle joined the family. He was twenty-five but he did not look more than eighteen. He had hair so fair it was almost white. He had one of those blank faces behind which nothing much might be happening, but actually he had taken a good degree at Oxford and thought a great deal. One of the things he thought about was how he would find a way to see the world. He had put his name down at an agency for a job abroad, but when he was told Sebastian wanted a tutor, though the engagement was only for while he was in England, he took the job as a specula-tion. After all, he told himself, they might take me abroad with the boy. You never know.

The only thing Paul had imagined he would hate about his engagement was Sebastian. 'I bet he's a spoilt little horror,' he told his friends. 'I shall be expected to trail around like a keeper of a performing monkey.' So when he met Sebastian he had a nice surprise.

Paul turned up with his luggage at Number 10 at teatime. Polly was at the art gallery. David was out on Sebastian's business, so the children and Miss Popple were having a large tea in the dining-room.

'Leave those cases there, dear,' Mrs Bottle said, accepting

Paul at once as one of the family. 'Mr B. will 'elp you up with them later.' Then she opened the dining-room door and pushed Paul into the room. 'He's come,' she said. 'I laid a place in case.'

Some young men might have felt shy with ten eyes fixed on them but not Paul. He shook Miss Popple by the hand, grinned at the children, then studied what was on the table.

'Four sorts of sandwich. A cut-and-come-again loaf and strawberry jam, three kinds of cake, that's my idea of a tea.' He sat in the empty chair which was between Wolfgang's and Myra's. 'Now don't tell me, I'm going to guess which of you is which.'

He did guess. Then he ate an enormous tea and then he suggested follow-my-leader, with him leading, round the garden to settle the tea.

'I can't come,' Sebastian said. 'It's my practice time.'

Paul pushed that aside.

'I reckon anyone can spare ten minutes for a good follow-my-leader.'

It could have been the way he said it, or perhaps Sebastian thought just for once it would be fun to play, but a minute later they were all fastened in a tail behind Paul, hopping, skipping and frog-jumping over Mr Bottle's flower-beds. Miss Popple, laughing, watched them from the window.

'If I don't take care he'll have me doing that in a day or two.'

Mrs Bottle, who came in to clear the tea, was astounded.

'Look at our Sebastian carryin' on like a real child. I shouldn't wonder if we couldn't do with that young man, Miss Popple.'

They could do with Paul in more ways than one Miss Popple discovered, for the very next week Wolfgang and Myra were called to the studio for fittings, and they were warned that Wolfgang would be needed for location shots, which meant that part of the film which would be made out of doors. This meant far more than Miss Popple not being there to teach lessons. It meant she was not there to talk about meals with Mrs Bottle, or to make laundry lists, or persuade Polly that red slacks, a yellow coat and a jade scarf were not a good mixture to wear when visiting her art gallery. It meant no Miss Popple to see that Ethel went off to school properly dressed with clean socks on, and clean tights in her case, and money on her for elevenses. It meant that all day long there was no one who was like a nice soft cushion on which any member of the household could hurl themselves and their troubles, certain of sympathy and often good, helpful advice. It meant, as well as no Miss Popple, no Myra, who was not only a good substitute for Miss Popple but was Wag's looker-after, and unless a dog has a proper looker-after he has a poor life in a big town.

Exactly what would have happened if there had not been Paul nobody tried to imagine. He took on or arranged everything.

'Don't flap, my dear Popkins,' he said. They were on Christian name or nickname terms in a week. 'Let's have the list and I'll see to everything. It'll be a kindness, my dear old thing, for I've nothing to do while Sebastian's practising.'

And he did see to everything, except the laundry list, which Miss Popple did overnight. He had sisters who often sneaked off to school in the wrong clothes or who left things behind, so he soon had Ethel sorted out.

'You will report to me with case undone and coat open,' he told her. 'And if I see even a speck on a sock or if one Monday you forget to take clean tights I'll have my tomahawk out and there'll be a scalping in the evening. Imagine my Ettie a dancer with no hair!'

Mrs Bottle adored Paul so talking about meals was fun for them both. Not that Mrs Bottle needed help in choosing meals, she didn't, but she thought it right that interest should be taken in her cooking by someone, so when Miss Popple was at the studio Paul went to the kitchen, sat on the table and, amidst a lot of laughter, talked food with Mrs Bottle.

Paul even proved, in the absence of Miss Popple, to be an adequate understudy for her as a cushion. 'Don't get in a state, Mrs F.,' he would say when Polly flapped around muttering: 'Where did I put those invitation cards to my show?' or, 'I know I put that list of names in this vase, somebody has moved it.' 'Just hold your horses a minute, and let bloodhound Paul have a look.'

It was Paul to whom Mumsmum moaned when she came round to have a look at Number 10 when nobody was about. 'I know they all try to be careful, but I don't know what my friends will say. Look at this paintwork. That's a scratch,' or 'Look at this chair. I'm afraid Wag has been allowed to sit on it.'

She always went away looking cheerful for Paul made marks on paint or furniture seem ridiculous. 'Nothing we can't put straight before we go. Anyway, seeing the enormous rent your friends are getting, I shouldn't think they're likely to say anything.' It was to Paul that Mr Bottle came about his dahlias. 'No one is fonder than I am of a dog, Mr Ingle, but that Wag 'e's fair savage on flower-beds. I can't give the show of dahlias what I should.' 'Exercise is what Wag needs,' Paul would answer. 'I've got to take Sebastian to the Albert Hall this afternoon. Wag shall come too and I'll race him across the Park and back while Sebastian is rehearsing. He won't have the strength to look at a dahlia when I'm through with him.'

But by far the best thing about Paul was the way he looked after Sebastian. In the mornings he gave him lessons, but most days these included a walk. History was his subject and he had a wonderful way, as he and Sebastian walked through the London streets, of rebuilding them so that Sebastian could see them as they had been hundreds of years before. When Sebastian had a rehearsal he disappeared, usually walking Wag. But he seemed to have an extra sense which made him know when the rehearsal was over and what he called the hickboo was about to begin. Hickboo was just musicians talking to each other. When that happened he would jerk a thumb towards the door and whisper 'Off,' and before he had time to think Sebastian would find himself outside. A car and chauffeur was hired for them all while they were in London. It took Ethel to and from her school and Polly to and from her gallery, and was supposed to take Sebastian wherever he had to go. But after Paul joined the family Sebastian only used the car when it was wet, on other days he and Paul walked or travelled on the top of a bus, something Sebastian had never done before and which he loved. It was only his fiddle which travelled home in the car. With Paul around Sebastian looked better, and though he was always hanging about waiting for the others to come home he was miles happier with them away all day than he had supposed he could be.

Ethel, in spite of the big girl's warning, was not only happy at Madame Fidolia's school but popular. It was, she discovered, grand to be a 'ballet special' and she was much the youngest. Quite soon even the big girls began to know her by sight and point her out to each other. The only thing Ethel did not like was being too young to have a licence. As it was the autumn term Christmas shows were in preparation. Almost every day a group, or sometimes just one pupil, was waiting to be inspected before an audition. Then everyone who passed called out, 'Good luck. I hope you get it.'

'It's sickening I'm only nine,' she told Myra one day. 'Three years before I can get one. Imagine!'

'But what would you want to do if you had a licence?'

'I'd like even to walk about in a ballet. It would make me know how it felt. There are lots of children in the "Nutcracker Suite". I'd like to be one of them. But I never will, for even if Operation Home comes off I'll be at The Royal Ballet School by then, and children from there aren't allowed to work.'

Myra looked admiringly at Ethel. It was extraordinary of her, she thought, not only to have settled down quickly in the school but to have such a good idea of what was going on. If she had been sent to a school she knew that she would be there at least a term before she knew where she was supposed to be for her classes, let alone find out about what was happening to other people.

'Who told you about The Royal Ballet School?'

'Madame Fidolia. I have two half-hours a week alone with her. It will be more next term. I learn her things, you know, her special way of doing something.'

They were in the garden playing with Wag. Myra stopped just as she was about to throw his rubber bone.

'Her way of doing things! But, Ettie, she can't still dance, can she?'

'Not like she used to, of course. But look.' Ethel chose a piece of lawn clear of flower-beds. 'This is a jump I learnt with everybody, even with Madame Leninskya.' She jumped in the air changing feet as she did so. 'Now this is Madame Fidolia's way. Watch the top of my head and you'll see I go higher.' Ethel jumped again and it was true, she did go higher.

'How's it done?'

But at that question Ethel's face looked as shut away as Sebastian's when he was playing his fiddle.

'Ways,' she said vaguely. 'To do with breathing and counting, you wouldn't understand.'

Myra, though she did not mind exactly, was feeling rather the odd one out in the family. Sebastian, of course, had always had his own life, but before, she, Wolfgang and Ethel had done things together. But now not only had Ethel got a busy, exciting world of her own, but so had Wolfgang. It had been all right when they had first gone to the studio. Mr Oslip had said they might as well do lessons there then they would be around for fittings, and Wolfgang could go to a studio elocutionist who would help him learn his part. In those first days they were given a large dressing-room in which a table had been put at which they did their lessons. After lessons they went to the wardrobe for fittings. This Miss Popple found fascinating, for under nylon covers there were literally thousands of costumes, some of which had been made for very famous actors and actresses. But Myra, and particularly Wolfgang who had four sets of clothes, found the fittings a bore, though Myra had to admit her frock was pretty. It was blue with rather a low neck, a sash and a sticking-out skirt which came half-way down to her ankles. Under it she had several petticoats, the top ones with lace on them, and frilly lace-edged drawers. Wolfgang had patched, shabby clothes for the beginning of the film, sailor suits for after he became famous and a Lord Fauntleroy for reciting in.

But after ten days of lessons in a dressing-room the outdoor filming began. For this they were taken by car to wherever the shooting was going on, and there they found the caravan waiting which was to be their schoolroom while on location. Myra struggled hard to get used to the caravan and to work as well as she had in all the different school-rooms she had known, but it was difficult, for caravans don't feel like schoolrooms. Wolfgang would not even try.

'It's no good, Popps,' he said. 'I don't feel like lessons dressed as Eddie.' Eddie was what the boy in the film was called. And Miss Popple quite understood, for though she was wearing her ordinary clothes she found what was going on outside much more interesting than teaching. So she compromised.

'We must work as hard as we can, but if I feel we have got behind we will do extra lessons in the Christmas holidays.'

For the first few days the outside shooting passed off quietly. Eddie, or Edward as he was called when he became a grown-up actor, had lived in what in those days had been a village just outside London. His mother was a widow and very poor, so Eddie, who was the eldest of the family, had to work hard to get food. He had worked for a farmer so all the shots were of him on the farm, cleaning pigsties, pulling turnips, mucking out yards and other hard jobs for a small boy. But by the fifth day of filming the farm scenes were finished and then they filmed a school playground and scenes in a churchyard, for Eddie had been a choir boy and it was the rector who had encouraged him to recite. Of course, for the school and choir scenes, other children were needed and in the school scenes there were a lot of other children. Myra and Miss Popple knew exactly what would happen directly they saw the children.

'Oh, Popps!' Myra said. 'This is Wolf's day. Imagine him the star and all those others just like me with nothing to say.'

'I am imagining,' Miss Popple agreed. 'And I don't like to think of what it will do to Wolfie.'

It went to Wolfgang's head like wine. He always had been a show-off but never before had he had a large audience to show off to. In no time he had a spellbound crowd listening while he took them in imagination round the world, giving sketches as he went of how people in different places behaved. As a result, by the time he was wanted for a scene in which the rector saw him reading poetry to his fellow choir boys, he was thoroughly overexcited. Mr Oslip put up with two terribly overacted rehearsals, but that was enough.

'Now, Wolfie,' he said, 'we'll have this scene played

properly. The rector doesn't see one of his choir boys giving an imitation of a character in an old silent film, he sees a small boy quietly reading poetry to his friends.'

But Wolfgang was not so easily calmed down. It was fun to make the other choir boys giggle, it was boring reading quietly. He was reading Robert Herrick's 'To Daffodils', which he thought both dull and silly, so he had helped it out with action. He had not seen Mr Oslip when he was cross before, so he did not recognise the warning light.

'"Fair daffodils,"' he read, '"we weep to see you haste away so soon."' He took out his handkerchief and with loud sniffs pretended to cry into it.

Mr Oslip came quietly to Wolfgang, took the book from his hands. Then he called his personal assistant.

'George.'

The assistant – an anxious-looking young man in a polo-necked sweater and horn-rimmed glasses – came running.

'Yes, Mr Oslip?'

'Who is Wolfie's stand-in?'

So that the principals would not get too tired hanging about while the cameras got into position, each one had a stand-in. But so far no standing-in had been needed, so Wolfgang had no idea he had a stand-in.

'It's Tom Perks. Shall I call him?'

'Please.'

While Tom Perks was being fetched an awkward silence fell on the choir boys, for each of them wondered what was going to happen and wished they had not giggled. Mr Oslip was apparently only interested in the book of poetry. He seemed to be reading it. Presently George came back with a red-headed boy who was almost exactly Wolfgang's height. Mr Oslip shut the poetry book.

'I can't waste time on a boy who fools about,' he said to Wolfgang, 'so I think we'll see what your stand-in can do with the part of Eddie.'

Wolfgang felt as if he was falling off a high building. One moment he had been Wolfgang Forum with a starring part, now he was nothing. He had not known such an awful thing could happen. For once he could not think what to say. Then one of the other boys muttered:

'It was our fault as much as his.'

Mr Oslip seemed to consider that.

'What have you to say, Wolfie?'

Wolfgang swallowed for there seemed something in his throat.

'I won't fool any more.'

'Right,' said Mr Oslip. 'See you don't. Now we'll rehearse that shot again.' He signalled to the actor who was playing the rector. 'From your entrance into the churchyard please. Quiet, everybody.'

Wolfgang had not particularly wanted to act in the film to start with, but now he was in it he was not going to risk having to come home saying he had had the part taken away from him. To Miss Popple and Myra, who had of course heard what had happened, he said in a proud voice:

'That Tom can be Eddie for all I care.' But inside he minded awfully and tried terribly hard not to behave badly again.

12

Looking For a Way

Sebastian's concert was a tremendous success. For years his records had been known by all music lovers, and of course his reputation had gone ahead of him. But few in the audience were taking a reputation made abroad on trust, Sebastian had to make a new reputation in his own country.

Sebastian was so small for twelve that when he first came on to the platform, the audience could not believe so young a child could have such an astounding reputation. One of Sebastian's great assets was that in a concert hall he was always so wrapped up in music that he was not entirely conscious of his audience, so after a brief bow in answer to polite welcoming applause he stood quietly listening, waiting to start playing.

All the family, including Mumsmum and Mumsdad, had seats for the concert, and Paul found standing room at the back. It was a splendid evening. In other countries it was easy to accept that some of the excitement caused by Sebastian's playing was because the audience was made up of foreigners known to be emotional. But the English were known not to be emotional, so the children were expecting less applause than usual. They were quite wrong. There was a slight pause before the clapping started, as if Sebastian had laid a spell on his audience, then with a crash the applause came, followed by shouts. Amazed, the children saw staid English men and women standing up, yelling, and sometimes crying. It was most surprising.

'But not a bit what you've taught us to expect, Popps,' Ethel told Miss Popple when they got home. 'More they were like South Americans, and you know how they get.'

That was the first time Paul had a chance to show what he could do after a concert. They all went round to the artists' room, where they found Sebastian looking white and miserable, crushed into one corner surrounded by people asking him questions, while David, his eyes shining with pride and happiness, was cut off in another corner. Of course the moment Polly came into the room she was cut off too as people poured over her. Paul looked round, measured the distance to the door, then dived through the people surrounding Sebastian, muttered 'Bed,' picked him up as if he had been a sack of carrots, and calling to the others to follow, charged out of the room. This made one of the papers write the next day:

'Young Sebastian has a bodyguard.' A story which stuck.

The next excitement was for Wolfgang. The outside shots were finished so filming in the studio started. This was much harder work, he found, for he had not spoken out of doors, as where sound was needed it would be recorded separately. Anyway, Wolfgang's had mostly been long shots which would be matched up in the studio for close-ups. His first day's shooting in the studio was the close-up of the scene in the churchyard that had got him into trouble. The rector had to dismiss the other choir boys and then talk to Eddie about the poem he had been reading. Mr Oslip explained this scene to Wolfgang before he rehearsed it.

'We may have a bit of trouble with this, Wolfie, because it's got to be dead right. You have to have enough cockney accent to let the rector see what he's up against.'

That did not worry Wolfgang.

'Mr Bottle – he's the gardener belonging to the house where we are – well, he talks cockney and so does Mrs Bottle. I can say it like they do.'

Mr Oslip had been afraid of something like that.

'A real cockney accent is hard to get rid of. Did you see *My Fair Lady* on your travels?'

'No.'

'Well, the lady in that story had a cockney accent, and all the play shows how difficult an accent is to get rid of. So Eddie must only have half an accent. Enough to let the rector see what he's up against, but not enough to hide the talent that is there. Now, let's hear a few lines.'

Wolfgang's first attempt was pure Bottle, and so was his second, then suddenly he understood what was wanted. Mr Oslip had his mouth open to say: 'No. That's still too cockney,' when Wolfgang stopped him.

'I know. I see how you want it. Just the littlest bit of Bottle and the rest me.' Then he recited the whole poem exactly as Mr Oslip did want it. He was so good in fact that after one rehearsal with the rector Mr Oslip said he would shoot the scene.

It was Wolfgang's success which led to action about Operation Home. Myra was standing watching the shooting. When it was finished Mr Oslip came over to her.

'Wolfie was good, didn't you think? If every scene goes like that we shall be ahead of schedule.'

Myra felt as if her tummy turned a somersault.

'You mean you mightn't want Wolf after Christmas?'

Mr Oslip was by this time thinking of the next shot.

'It's possible.'

Myra was appalled. It had been almost promised the film would last until after Christmas. It was Wolf's film which was the beginning of Operation Home, they had no other way to get it started. Although it was only October the wireless and the announcers on the Bottles' television were giving out how many shopping days it was to Christmas. The things Mumsdad had arranged had turned out all right. Ethel was happy at school, Sebastian getting on well with Paul and she and Wolfgang were doing as many lessons as they could at the studio, but these things were not getting them anywhere for no one had heard David or Polly talk about a change of plans, in fact, the opposite. Polly was always saying things like: 'How pleased Madame Leninskya will be, Ettie, when you see her at Christmas, to find you've got on so well.' 'Dermidoff will love to hear about your reception here, Sebastian. You must remember to tell him everything when we get to Paris.' 'I think Paul's a dear, Miss Popple, but you'll be glad when we get to Paris and you can have all four in your own schoolroom again, won't you?'

Then there were the letters from Mr Ruttenstein.

'It's Russia for us next year,' David said one morning. 'We shall have to put you on a diet this time, Myra. We can't have you being sick all the time.'

Another letter told of a return visit to Japan.

'You'll like that, Wolf. I hope you can still make that mysterious greeting hiss.'

One day a letter came to David about a next year Rest Period plan.

'Our first Rest Period next year looks like being in San Francisco. Misken suggests a repeat performance of the concerto first. That's good news for you children, I don't want you to miss hearing him conduct it.'

Long before Mr Oslip said Wolf's part in the film might finish sooner than he had expected Myra had been worried.

'I feel so awful when they talk like that,' she told Mumsdad. 'I mean, their not knowing what we're planning, or worse, our plan not coming off.'

Mumsdad was getting bothered himself. He hated not saying right out what he was planning. But it seemed silly to barge in too soon, almost certainly making Polly angry with him, when the change of plans would come naturally as soon as Mr Oslip said he would need Wolf in the New Year. However, when Myra came rushing to him to tell him what Mr Oslip had said, he saw action had to be taken.

'I suppose I'll have to tackle your mother, but I don't feel hopeful, when there's no excuse for keeping you three here.'

Myra sounded despairing.

'Grandfather said when I decided the time had come to have a regular home, if I honestly meant it, a way would be shown me to make it happen, so I was sure Wolf's film was the way.'

'Maybe it still is. You said Mr Oslip only said it was possible it would be finished by Christmas.'

Myra doubted that.

'Wolfie's very good, they hardly ever do many retakes of his scenes.'

'I feel I've let you all down,' Mumsdad confessed. 'From what Mr Oslip said, I was so certain Wolfie would be filming in the first part of next year so it looked plain sailing for, as Miss Popple would have to stay with you and Wolf, it would have been simple to suggest Ettie stayed too. Then I meant to have suggested finding a house and Bob's your uncle. But I can't see my getting far if I try and keep you here for no reason.'

Myra sounded depressed.

'Mummy'll say: "But they love travelling," and that about families all being together.'

Then Mumsdad had an idea.

'I wonder if your grandfather could help. It's the Bath concert next week. I hear he and your grandmother are going to be there. Why not ask if you can go? It's natural to want to see them. He may have an idea about our next step.'

So a week later Myra went with Sebastian, Polly, David and Paul to Bath. Grandmother and Grandfather came the next day. At first they were so pleased to see David, Polly and Sebastian, and there was such a lot to hear about, that Myra could not get Grandfather to herself. Then Sebastian had a rehearsal, and David and Paul went with him. Grandmother and Polly settled down for a good family talk, so Myra and Grandfather went to look at the Roman baths and on the way she poured out their troubles.

'It looked perfect, like I wrote to you. But now it could go wrong. Wolf's so good in the film.'

Grandfather thought about things before he answered.

'It would seem as though the time had come for you to tell your father and mother what you want.'

Myra looked up at Grandfather. How could she make him see the hopelessness of that idea? He had not toured the world with them for four years so, however often they told him, he could not see how sure Polly was that they were the luckiest family in the world to live as they did. He had not heard her say over and over again: 'Yes, aren't they lucky children, but aren't I lucky too? I would never have allowed Sebastian to play in public if it meant breaking up the family. I couldn't be happy unless all the children were with me.'

'We couldn't tell them. Not without a reason. Mummy just wouldn't believe we wanted not to tour, and if she did believe it she'd mind terribly.'

Grandfather nodded.

'I see that.' He thought again. 'Why don't you have a talk to Mr Oslip? Ask him right out how long he's going to want Wolfie.'

'Goodness! You don't know anything about film studios. People as unimportant as me don't talk to Mr Oslip unless they're spoken to. I'm a very low sort of worm there. Mr Oslip only knows my name because I'm Wolf's sister.'

'Then let Wolfie do it. He can speak to Mr Oslip, can't he?'

'Of course, he talks to him all the time. The only snag is to make Wolf ask sensibly. In some ways he's very young for eleven, and I think it's making him younger being Eddie, who's only eight.'

Grandfather laughed.

'I can imagine. But Wolfie's no fool. You try letting somebody else do the work for a change. If Wolf understands the importance of what he's to do it's my opinion he'll come back with a straight answer.'

'And if Mr Oslip says he'll be finished before Christmas?'

Grandfather was silent for quite a long time. Then he said:

'I don't know. But don't lose heart, Myra. A way will be found, I'm certain of it. Let's first hear what Mr Oslip tells Wolfie.'

Grandfather managed, which was not easy, to have a talk with Sebastian. He arranged it by asking for it. It was the morning after the concert.

'Need you rush off, David? I haven't had a chance to talk to my grandson. How about a walk, Sebastian?'

'I wanted to practise before I left,' Sebastian explained.

'Well, just once suppose you miss it,' Grandfather suggested. 'It's time you and I knew each other. Do you realise I've not seen you since you were eight?'

'It's disgraceful,' David agreed. 'Hop along, Sebastian. There'll be time for you to practise this evening.'

It was cold, not nice weather for a walk, and Sebastian's face was becoming so well known, if they sat down in a public building he was likely to be mobbed for autographs, so Grandfather took him into a church. Sebastian supposed, as Grandfather was a clergyman, he ought to know if it was all right using a church to talk in, but he was surprised.

'Is it all right? I mean, won't they mind our sitting here just to talk?'

'God won't,' said Grandfather, 'and I don't care what anyone else thinks.' Then he looked at Sebastian. 'How's it feel to be world famous?'

It was the sort of question people asked after concerts. The type of question usually Sebastian hated. But somehow, when Grandfather asked it, he didn't mind.

'It sort of happened, and now I'm used to it and don't think about it.'

'It's been a very lucrative happening. Have you thought what you're going to do with all the money you've earned?'

Sebastian felt as he did when his father talked about money. It was not a thing grown-ups should talk about to children.

'Daddy looks after it.'

Grandfather raised his eyebrows.

'All the same, it's yours. And money is a responsibility. You should be thinking how you intend to use it. Are you going on touring or are you planning to take a year or two off for study?'

Sebastian looked unhappy. Surely Grandfather must know it was not he who made plans.

'Mr Ruttenstein hasn't said.'

'I should not think Mr Ruttenstein would have a say in such a matter. It will be for you and your father to decide surely.'

'It could be that next year, or more likely the year after, I could take time off. I would like to be a student at a music school. You talked to Myra about a regular home – what Mumsdad calls Operation Home – I think then it would be nice to have a house. To put things in drawers and find them there when you came back.'

'Does the plan of a music school hang on Mr Ruttenstein?'

'Yes.'

Sebastian had felt sure when Mr Ruttenstein had said one day he would give him his Amati it was not meant to be repeated to the grown-ups. He looked cautiously at Grandfather out of the sides of his eyes. He had a very safe face, he looked like a man who could keep a secret.

'If I tell you something will you absolutely swear not to tell Daddy? I think he wasn't meant to know, because he'd be angry if he knew. You see, he thinks I could say any day there'll be no more concerts.'

'I shan't say a word. You can trust me.'

Sebastian was already talking quietly because of being in a church. Now, as he spoke of the Amati, he used an awed whisper.

'It's the only fiddle I want. Such tone, Grandfather. You would think it spoke from Heaven.'

Grandfather understood that.

'Why don't you ask your father to buy it for you?'

Sebastian laughed out loud, then, shocked, put his hands to his mouth to stifle the sound.

'It would cost millions of dollars, I can't have earned what it's worth. Anyway, Mr Ruttenstein wouldn't sell. Why would he when he wants me to go on playing? You see, it is while I am a child he can cash in. When I'm grown-up I won't be so interesting.'

Grandfather did not like that.

'I must say your Mr Ruttenstein doesn't sound a fit person to own a superlative fiddle. Have you anything else you want?'

'The house. I don't want it now, but I do see the others are tired of travelling. It's not nice touring without them but I would like to buy a house for them, if that's what they want. I could stay in it for Rest Periods.'

Grandfather sat thinking for a bit. Then he said:

'I wish you'd let me have a talk with your father about the Amati. It might help everybody.'

Sebastian was appalled.

'But you promised. You wouldn't break a promise. Clergymen don't.'

'I wouldn't dream of breaking it. I asked your permission to break it. I wouldn't ask if I didn't think it was important.'

Sebastian looked scared.

'No, you can't. You don't know Mr Ruttenstein. If I annoyed him, perhaps I would never get the Amati. I must have it, Grandfather. I must.'

Grandfather seemed to want to say more, then he changed his mind and got up.

'All right then, you must.' He led the way out of the church. 'It's time we were going back and I need the walk, for I am feeling unchristian about your Mr Ruttenstein.' Then he seemed to push Mr Ruttenstein away as if he smelled bad. 'I do like your tutor, and I can see you two get on like a house on fire.'

That evening, when they got back to London, Myra told Wolfgang that Grandfather wanted him to talk to Mr Oslip. Wolfgang barely bothered to listen.

'Of course I will. I'll do it tomorrow.'

Myra was not satisfied.

'Not just ask as if it didn't matter. Grandfather meant ask properly so you get a real answer.'

'Of course I'll ask properly. Him and me talk a lot.'

'I know you do,' Myra agreed. 'But this is terribly important, you must see that. For if he says you'll finish by Christmas an absolutely new reason has to be found to start Operation Home. You do see that. I mean, what reason can we give for not going to Paris for the Rest Period unless it's because of you?'

'How you do go on,' Wolfgang grumbled. 'Natter. Natter. Natter. I've said I'll ask Mr Oslip, so shut up.'

But though Wolfgang spoke as if asking Mr Oslip was nothing, inside he knew it might be difficult. It was true Mr Oslip talked to him a lot but always about Eddie. How Eddie felt, and what Eddie thought. He never seemed to worry about what Wolfgang thought. But of course he didn't tell Myra that.

Four days and a Sunday passed before Wolfgang had a chance to talk to Mr Oslip. They had reached that part of the film where Eddie was just beginning to recite in public. By then he and his family were living in London proper. But the rector was still taking an interest in him, and there was a scene in which he came to London to ask the elocution master, whom afterwards Eddie found dead, to teach him, and Wolfgang was not in the scene. Then Eddie's first reciting engagements were in rough places, which meant crowd scenes, which kept Mr Oslip so busy he talked to nobody, and even Wolfgang could not get up his courage to say anything. Then two days were spent on the other characters appearing at an old-fashioned music-hall, where Eddie was to make his name as Little Eddie, the boy reciter.

Wolfgang always hated the days when he was not used much, so he grumbled and groused and made life tough for Miss Popple. But those four days he found particularly trying for, having said he'd ask Mr Oslip the next day, he felt humiliated he couldn't do it.

'It's no good looking and looking at me, Myra,' he grumbled. 'I can't talk to him unless I'm on the set. Even you must see that.'

Myra was fed up with his crossness.

'Of course I see. But I don't see why you should be so beastly to me and Popps. It's not our fault you're not wanted.'

They were in the canteen having mid-morning milk. Wolfgang kicked the leg of their table.

'It's so boring. We might just as well do lessons at home.'

'I like that,' said Myra. 'What about me? Coming here every day knowing I'm only going to be wanted once.'

But on the fifth filming day Wolfgang got his chance. He was called on to the floor early, dressed for the first time in his Lord Fauntleroy suit. Mr Oslip called him over to see how he looked.

'Very nice. I wish your hair was longer but it's in keeping that it would not be very long to start with. I'd like to get it to your shoulders for the Windsor Castle scene, so we won't shoot that until the last minute.'

That was obviously Wolfgang's cue.

'When do you think the last minute will be?'

But Mr Oslip was thinking only of his picture.

'I know you have learnt what you are to recite, but have you thought about what is going on outside the music-hall where you recite?'

Most days Wolfgang, Myra and Miss Popple saw what were called 'rushes', which was uncut film made the day before. Although Wolfgang had not worked much in the last four days they had still seen the 'rushes', so he was able to answer that.

'It's the Boer War. People crying and men in funny uniforms marching.'

'That's right. That war was young Eddie's chance. That patriotic stuff that you recite was just what the audience wanted. Eddie became a star overnight.'

Wolfgang knew that. He tried to get back to Windsor.

'How long does hair take to grow? I mean, how long before mine is to my shoulders?'

That interested Mr Oslip. He turned Wolfgang round again.

'Faster than you'd think. You've only been growing it a couple of months and already it curls up round your neck.'

Wolfgang thought Mr Oslip was being tiresome.

'What I want to know is how long will I be in this film? It's important because ...'

At that exact moment Mr Oslip's Production Manager came up to him with the continuity girl. Someone who had been in the music-hall scene yesterday could not be there today. What would Mr Oslip like done? In a second Mr Oslip had forgotten Wolfgang's question and was thinking only of his own problem.

'Did you ask him?' Myra asked when Wolfgang was

sent back to do his lessons, while Tom, the stand-in, took his place.

Wolfgang had picked up a few useful phrases since he had been working in a film studio.

'We're in conference,' he answered grandly.

But after tea he got his chance. It had been a difficult day's shooting, but Wolfgang had been good and Mr Oslip was pleased with him.

'Do a good day like that tomorrow and I'll give you a present. What would you like?'

'What I most want just now,' said Wolfgang, 'is to know just how long you think you'll want me in this film.'

Mr Oslip's face was expressive. Now it was all thinking about Wolfgang's question.

'That's hard to say, Wolfie. So many things can hold us up.'

'Don't you even know a kind of time?'

'Not really. Not at this stage. I know when I'm aiming to finish with you.'

Wolfgang spoke in a burst, as if he was soda water coming out of a siphon.

'When?'

'The end of February.'

Wolfgang was enchanted.

'Goody! Goody! I must go and tell Myra.'

Mr Oslip looked in surprise at Wolfgang's back.

'Amusing boy that,' he said to his Production Manager. 'I offered him a present, but all he wanted was to know when I'd have done with him. And I was all set to bring him an electric train or some such.'

13

Breaking the News

Mumsdad, when he heard the news about February, said the time had come to tell David everything. In the busy Forum day it was not easy to get hold of anybody, but Mumsdad was a determined sort of man.

'We want you to come to us one evening this week,' he said on the telephone in an I-won't-take-no voice.

'There's no concert on Wednesday or Thursday. I think Polly and I are free on Wednesday. Would that do?'

'Splendidly. But we want you alone, no Polly.'

David was puzzled at that.

'Why?'

'We have our reasons. If Polly is inquisitive let her think we are discussing her Christmas present.'

Polly was inquisitive so David did that, and on the Wednesday night walked over after supper to see Polly's parents.

Mumsdad wasted no time for he had thought carefully beforehand what he would say.

'I'm afraid this is going to upset Polly. But this fellow Oslip will probably need Wolfie until at least the end of February.'

'February! But he can't. We're going to Paris in December. Sebastian is having lessons as usual with Dermidoff.'

'I know that is the idea,' Mumsdad agreed, 'but I think your other three have different plans. Wouldn't it be possible for you to stay on here for the Rest Period and let Sebastian have lessons from someone else?'

The idea was so new to David he took time to take it in. Mumsmum tried to help.

'You see, dear, Myra and Wolfie will have to be here, and it won't be easy to persuade Ettie to leave that dancing school.'

'We've got so used to Dermidoff and having our Rest Period in Paris,' David explained. 'But if Wolfie has got to stay on for his film I suppose we might think about London.'

'I believe you could have the house for a bit longer,' said Mumsmum. 'The owners are thinking of settling in the Bahamas and, if they do, they are going to sell it.'

'It's this "end of February" that's worrying me,' David explained. 'At the beginning of February, as you know, we're off on another Far East tour.'

Mumsmum pressed on.

'It looks as if Sebastian will have to make that tour without the other three.'

David looked dreadfully worried.

'I hope not. Polly would never stand for it. At the worst I suppose Sebastian could start off with myself and Paul, and Polly could fly the other three out in April.'

Mumsdad saw there would have to be plain speaking.

'I think, if you ask them, you'll find the other three don't want to be flown out.'

'They want a home,' Mumsmum said gently. 'It's natural, David, dear, they haven't had one for four years. It's a long time.'

David pushed his fingers through his hair until it stood on end.

'I can't believe it! I thought they were as happy as Polly and I. Seeing the world ...'

Mumsdad stopped him.

'Becoming world citizens – learning geography from travel and not from an atlas. We've heard all that, David, but, though it was true once, it's not true now. Your mother-in-law's right. What your children want is a home.'

David spoke on a sort of accepting gasp.

'All right. I take your word for it that is what they are thinking at the moment. What am I to say to Polly? She'll never agree to splitting the family up, but Ruttenstein has engagements for Sebastian for all next year and pencilled in for the year after. What do you suggest is the best way to break this news to your daughter?'

Mumsdad and Mumsmum looked at each other. Who should speak? Then Mumsdad gave Mumsmum a you-do-it nod.

'I wouldn't break the news all in one piece, dear. Polly has strong views about keeping her family together, I know, and quite right too if it's possible. But once she gets used to something we've always found she accepted plans made for her. Couldn't you just cancel the Paris arrangements for a start?'

'Keep the house on if possible,' Mumsdad put in, 'for if she decides to go to the Far East with Sebastian she won't mind so much leaving the others if it's in a house that she knows, with Miss Popple in charge and us round the corner.'

'The next step must be to buy a house,' Mumsmum went on. 'In London, I suppose, anyway somewhere near, where Sebastian can spend his Rest Periods.'

David sat up at that suggestion and looked at Mumsdad.

'I don't think I can do that, can I? It's always been accepted that Sebastian's money could be used to help have his family round him, but I don't think we could use it for a house he would scarcely see. I earn enough to keep the other three, but I've got no capital to buy a house with.'

Mumsdad laughed.

'You were never any good about money, David, it's lucky you've put me in charge of Sebastian's earnings. He's got enough to buy any number of houses, and a well-chosen house would be a good investment for him. He can let his family live in it or, if you insist, you could pay him rent, but, anyway, the property is his, and its value might increase.'

David always believed Mumsdad when he talked about money.

'I would be responsible for all expenses of course. As a matter of fact, one good thing if this happens would be that the other three would learn what it's like to be hard up. All this trailing after Sebastian could have allowed them to think they were rich.'

Again Mumsdad laughed.

'Sebastian is not the only one making money. Wolfie is

doing all right. If he's a success I dare say he'll get the offer of another film.'

'And I gather Ettie is very promising,' said Mumsmum. 'In about eight years she may be a star.'

David got up.

'You've knocked the wind out of me. It's all been so unexpected.'

'Have a talk with the children before you start on Polly,' Mumsdad advised. 'They'll tell you how it all started. You'll be surprised.'

David took Mumsdad's advice and he was surprised. He caught Myra the next morning taking Wag for his first morning 'out'. He kissed her.

'I saw Mumsdad and Mumsmum last night. They told me you three are tired of touring. Is it true?'

Now it was said out loud it was a relief, but kind of frightening.

'Yes.' Myra felt her cheeks turning red, as if she had done something wrong. 'We were sort of thinking it and then Grandfather said it.'

'Your grandfather! What did he say?'

'Lots in little bits, and then something special to me.'

'Can you tell me?'

Myra tried to remember exactly.

'First he and Granny said how you had always wanted to travel, even when you were little, but was Mummy getting tired of it.'

David smiled at that.

'I can't see Mummy ever getting tired of travelling, can you?'

'No, we said that,' Myra agreed. 'So then Grandfather asked if we liked it, and Wolf said he was beginning to abhor it.'

David was amazed.

'Can you imagine why, if that is how you were feeling, you didn't tell me and Mummy?'

Myra turned redder than before. How could she explain that until Grandfather helped it seemed impossible to suggest an end of travelling?

'We thought you couldn't split a family up, so as Sebastian had to travel we had to. But Granny said we'd have to stop sooner or later to be properly educated, not only lessons – like Ettie's dancing. Ettie said Madame Leninskya had said she had talent and should go presently to The Royal Ballet School.'

David made a despairing gesture.

'But why, if Madame Leninskya said this, didn't Ettie tell me?'

Myra felt stupid and helpless.

'Because she didn't think she could go because of families being together. Then one day Grandfather started about Wolf.'

'What – to become a film star?'

Too late Myra remembered what Wolf did want to be.

'Of course not, that was an accident because of meeting Mr Oslip in the train. It was just sort of general. That was when Grandfather asked us about the parable.'

'Which one?'

'About talents – the man who had five and made it ten, and the one who buried his in the ground.'

'Did he! He used to talk to me about that when I was a small boy. The idea was to see that I practised the piano.'

'The idea for us, I think,' said Myra, 'was to make us remember we had talents and not just to think Sebastian had enough for us all.'

'Surely you didn't need to be told that?'

Myra rubbed her cheek against her father's arm.

'Silly Daddy, of course we didn't. Except me because, quite truthfully, I haven't got what most people mean by a talent. That's what Grandfather talked to me specially about.'

David's face showed how fond he was of her.

'What did he say?'

'I'd said I was dull and didn't do anything, and he said a talent didn't need to be for one of the arts, it could be for wisdom and being a good sister. Do you think that's true?'

'I know it is.'

'I've found it a great comfort Grandfather said that,' Myra admitted. 'You need to remember often that talents don't need to be for the arts, when you spend every day in a studio where you only have a part that doesn't say anything.'

'I can imagine. But you fixed to do it, I didn't. Even now you could do lessons with Sebastian. I'm sure they could find another Princess.'

'Oh, they could, but I won't do that. Grandfather would be ashamed of me. You see, he really was the person who got Wolf and me into a film.'

'How?'

'Because he said: "When you decide the time has come that you need a regular home, and honestly mean it, a way will be shown you to make it happen." Then I was shown Mr Oslip and it is beginning to happen.'

David looked wistfully at Myra.

'I wish I knew why your grandfather, who is my father remember, couldn't have told me all these things.'

Myra again rubbed her face against his sleeve.

'I think he thought it was good for us to try and help ourselves. But he did say "Make a wise plan, Myra, and your father will fall in with it."'

David gave her hair an affectionate rub.

'So he will, but we must go cautiously so that we get Mummy to fall in too.'

David had not missed that Myra had not told him exactly what Grandfather had said to Wolfgang. If there was no thought of a film career at the time, what other ambition had Wolfgang? The best way was to ask him.

Wolfgang usually went straight to the kitchen when he came back from the studio, for the Bottles were much more interested in hearing what had happened each day than anybody else in the house. Besides, if he got home early enough, he could go into their sitting-room where, if he was lucky, there was a cowboy film on their television set. It just showed, Wolfgang said, the sort of people the Marshalls were who owned the house, that they had no television in their living-room.

'If this was my house,' he had told the Bottles, 'there'd be a television in every single room.'

That day the scene they had shot had been of Eddie reciting a patriotic poem in the music-hall. Wolfgang had loved every minute of it for there were crowds of extras as audience, as well as the artists who were supposed to be appearing on the same programme as Eddie.

'I wear my Lord Fauntleroy suit of course, and while I'm reciting the ladies all cry, especially the ones standing in the wings. Then when I get to the end of the poem a great enormous Union Jack comes down behind me, then the orchestra plays "God Save the Queen" and ...'

That was when David interrupted. He put his head round the kitchen door.

'Sorry to interrupt the recital but I'm going out to get some cigarettes, Wolfie. Like to come with me? Some air will do you good after spending all day in the studio.'

'That's right, Wolfie,' Mrs Bottle agreed. 'You go with your Dad. You can tell me and Mr B. the rest when you come back.'

As soon as they were out of the house David said:

'I hear you don't want to tour any more. Is that right?'

Wolfgang had not supposed his father had anything special to say, so he was most surprised, but not at all fussed.

'Absolutely true. But I didn't know you knew yet. Who told you?'

'Mumsdad, Mumsmum and Myra. But I understand the idea started with Grandfather.'

'That's right. I'd known for ages inside I wanted a way to be me, but he talked about it.'

'My dear Wolfie, of all my family I should say you'd been the most determinedly yourself since birth.'

'To you, yes, Daddy, but not to Mr Ruttenstein.'

That puzzled David.

'What's Mr Ruttenstein got to do with you?'

Wolfgang was so disgusted at such a question that

167

he stood still in the middle of the pavement. His voice throbbed with rage.

'To do with me! I like that! What hasn't he got to do with me? He sends me about as if I was a parcel in the post. And he's never cared what happened to me, to him I'm just part of Sebastian, like a tail's part of a dog.'

David put his hand on Wolfgang's shoulder and propelled him forward.

'Even if that's true there's no need to block up the pavement. But tell me, if you felt like this why didn't you tell Mummy and me?'

'We didn't seem able to somehow. We were always travelling, and it looked as if we always would. Then in Devonshire Grandfather made us see it needn't go on.'

'What did he say exactly about you? I mean, did he want you to go to a boarding school or what?'

Wolfgang felt as if he were back in Devonshire. Almost he could smell the oily scent of lavender as he squeezed handfuls into one of Granny's bags.

'He asked what I was going to be when I grew up.'

'What did you say?'

Wolfgang saw where talking had led him.

'You won't like what I said.'

'Let's hear it anyway.'

'I'm going to write pop songs.'

David made a face.

'Ugh! I hope you're not.'

'Grandfather didn't say that, he said if my talent – he was talking about that parable – was for writing pop music I had to write the best pop music I could.'

'I suppose that's true, but I hope it doesn't happen. I shouldn't like a son of mine to be responsible for adding to the musical trash in the world.'

'I knew that's how you'd feel, but if it happens I'm afraid you'll just have to be brave about it.'

David nodded.

'I expect I will, but we needn't worry about that now. Our trouble is how to make Mummy agree to you three stopping here while Sebastian goes to the Far East.'

David talked to Ethel in bed when he went up to kiss her good night. She had already heard from Myra and Wolfgang that Operation Home had begun. David sat on the edge of her bed.

'Are you enjoying the dancing school?'

'It's gorgeous. I don't like ordinary lessons much, I liked learning them from Popps, but Madame's special dancing classes are superb, and I like the acting and character dancing classes.'

'But you could learn just as well anywhere, couldn't you?'

Ethel sat up and hugged her knees.

'Not really. It's time I studied properly. If you go to all kinds of places to learn you don't get style and discipline, that's what Madame Leninskya said.'

'If – and mind you it's still only if – I could arrange for a permanent home in London, would you like to stay on with Madame Fidolia?'

Ethel was most emphatic about that.

'Oh, no. Nobody who's going to be a real dancer stays there. I must have an audition next year for The Royal Ballet School.' Her voice changed to an awed whisper.

'Do you know, Madame Leninskya told me in Paris she would write to Dame Ninette de Valois about me. Imagine the glory!'

David did not know much about ballet, but of course he knew that name.

'Imagine!' he said in a suitably respectful voice. 'But explain to me, darling. If Madame Leninskya was telling you these things last winter, why didn't you tell me?'

Ethel swivelled her eyes to look at her father.

'I don't know, except when she said it we just knew it wasn't any good telling anyone.'

'But after talking to Grandfather you felt you could tell me?'

Ethel thought about that.

'Not really. Even in Devonshire Wolf and me supposed we'd always be touring with Sebastian. It was Myra telling Wolf he could be in a film if he wanted to who sort of started us seeing we needn't.'

David kissed her.

'Lie down, it's time you were asleep. We've got to keep it a secret from Mummy at present, but perhaps The Royal Ballet School will happen.'

The last person David talked to that night was Miss Popple. He found her ironing one of her blouses in the schoolroom. He told her to go on ironing and sat on the schoolroom table.

'Tell me, Miss Popple, aren't we old enough friends for you to have told me my children wanted a home?'

Miss Popple paused in her ironing.

'It sounds silly now it's come out – but you and Mrs Forum

seemed so happy about the touring we didn't like to hurt you, I think.'

'You make us sound as if it was we who were children.'

That was so exactly how Miss Popple did think of David and Polly that she giggled.

'How silly that sounds ...'

'But it's true, isn't it?'

Miss Popple went back to her ironing.

'In a way I suppose it is.'

David got off the table.

'I can see I've a lot to learn yet, but from now onwards I shall be in charge of Operation Home.'

14

Christmas

Polly accepted the change of plans for the Rest Period without fuss. David had found out from Dermidoff that it would do Sebastian good to have lessons from a British fiddle teacher called Beaumont, so he mentioned this casually.

'There's a change of plans, darling. We're going to spend our Rest Period here. Telephone your mother and see if the Marshalls will let us stay on.'

Mumsmum was, of course, expecting that call.

'I know it will be all right. The Marshalls are going to settle in the Bahamas. Actually, they'd like to sell the house with everything in it.'

Polly laughed.

'That's something we don't want. We shall all be off again in February.'

'I wish you didn't have to go,' said Mumsmum. 'It's been so lovely having you all here.'

'We've loved it too,' Polly agreed. 'But by February we'll

all have had enough of staying in one place. Once travelling is in your blood you can't get it out.'

Tactfully Mumsmum dropped the subject.

'I'll write to the Marshalls today to say you are staying on. They'll be delighted.'

Everybody was pleased, especially the Bottles.

'Well, that's good 'earing,' Mrs Bottle said. 'I must get the things for me plum pudding today, lovely Christmas we'll 'ave.'

Mr Bottle was beaming.

'Proper treat the 'ouse will look decorated for Christmas. The Marshalls wouldn't 'ave decorations, but what I say is, Christmas isn't Christmas without.'

Miss Popple, when she heard this, said she did hope Mr Bottle would be careful, remembering it was not their house, for holly might scratch the paint.

It was a Sunday when she said this. Polly and David were out, but the children, Miss Popple and Paul were having a splendid tea with muffins in the dining-room.

'I would have thought a little scratching at Christmas wouldn't matter,' said Wolfgang. 'When we lived in Apple Bough we had holly absolutely everywhere, and nobody fussed.'

Miss Popple smiled at that.

'Well, dear, let us be fair, Apple Bough, lovely as it was, was very scratched at all times.'

Myra turned with shining eyes to Sebastian.

'Do you remember us all looking out of the window when Daddy dressed up as Father Christmas to cut the holly, and we thought he was real?'

Sebastian nodded.

'We made chains. They went all across the ceiling. Of course we're too busy to make anything now, but perhaps you can buy them ready made.'

Ethel had remembered something too.

'We had an angel on our Christmas tree.'

Myra said to Paul:

'You can't think what gorgeous things we had on our Christmas trees. The same every year.'

'Where are they?' Paul asked.

The children answered together.

'In store.'

'Like everything else that belongs to us,' Wolfgang added.

'We must buy some new ones,' said Sebastian. 'There are plenty in the shops.'

Miss Popple thought it best to speak before things went too far.

'We might get one of those charming artificial trees made of silver like we bought in Los Angeles. They're so clean.'

Eight reproachful eyes were turned on her.

'Popps, dear!' said Myra. 'For our first Christmas back in England we don't want a tree because it's clean.'

Miss Popple remembered other Christmases in rented houses.

'Real Christmas trees shed needles which make a terrible mess. They stick to a carpet as if they were glued there.'

'Then we'll put down a sheet or something,' Myra said firmly. 'But we won't have a sham tree.'

Miss Popple looked round the dining-room. Too well she knew that Christmas meant sticking things like nails into walls.

'This is a particularly well-furnished house. I do think we must all agree to be careful over Christmas.'

But Paul was on the children's side.

'My dear old Popps! The Marshalls are in the Bahamas. What the eye doesn't see the heart doesn't grieve after.'

'But they want to sell the place,' Miss Popple reminded him. 'How shocking if they missed a sale because we had left the house in poor condition.'

'We won't,' said Paul. 'I'm a dab with a paint brush. And I promise you after Christmas the children and I will search the carpet like ant-eaters after ants, looking for Christmas tree needles.'

David had supposed that Polly would have said something about the way Wolfgang's film was hanging on, which would give him his chance to hint that Myra, Wolfgang and Ethel might not be coming on Sebastian's tour. But Polly did not seem surprised.

'I suppose,' she said casually to her mother, 'the children have told Mr Oslip we're staying until February so he isn't hurrying.'

Mumsmum looked at her daughter, wondering, not for the first time, how a child of hers could be so vague. Surely Polly must have heard about the appalling expense of film making. As if Mr Oslip would take longer than he could possibly help; however, she did not argue but, knowing Polly was going on to a picture show, she telephoned David.

'You'll have to speak plainly or let her father do it. It's nearly December, it's time she knew.'

David knew this was true.

'I shall tell her myself directly Christmas is over, but

I want this to be the sort of Christmas the children will remember all their lives, which it won't be if Polly is in a state. You ought to have seen her before the children went to Devonshire. You'd have thought we were shipping all three to the other end of the world for life.'

And it was a glorious Christmas. It started when Mrs Bottle said:

'I shall need you all for a stir Monday. This one comin' is stir-up Sunday.'

They were having breakfast at the time. For a moment Miss Popple was sure the children were going to disgrace her. But Wolfgang remembered.

'The stir-up collect, you mean?'

Mrs Bottle beamed.

'That's it. You can't stir your pudding, not before that's been said.'

So that next Monday evening they all went to the kitchen to stir.

The pudding mixture was not in a kitchen bowl but in an old-fashioned china washstand basin. It had pink flowers on it. Mrs Bottle said she kept it special. She had her sleeves rolled up and she was stirring a great mass of rich, dark pudding with a wooden spoon.

'Youngest first,' she said. 'Take 'old of the spoon, Ettie. Then shut your eyes and wish.'

Mr Bottle had come to watch.

'But don't tell nobody what you wished or you won't get it.'

Ethel had to use both hands to stir. She shut her eyes tight. 'I'd like,' she wished, 'to be part of a real ballet.' She thought about this wish so long that Wolfgang got impatient.

'That's enough. It's my turn.' He gripped the spoon, stirred the pudding, shut his eyes, then found he had nothing to wish for. But just as he was giving up he remembered his popular songs. 'I'd like some day to be the most famous pop song writer in the world,' he wished.

Sebastian had no difficulty in knowing what he wanted. He took the spoon, shut his eyes and stirred. 'The Amati. Please, please, pudding, let Mr Ruttenstein give me the Amati.'

'I wonder what you wished,' Wolfgang said. 'You had a face on as if you were in a church.'

Myra felt it was no good expecting too much of a plum pudding. 'Please, pudding,' she wished, 'could you arrange I could see Apple Bough again?'

Then the grown-ups took over. Paul wished he might go abroad with Sebastian. Miss Popple's wish was for a home for the children. Polly wished to be asked to have another picture show and David that everybody would have a perfect Christmas. Finally, Wag was lifted on to the table and Myra held his paws on the spoon while she stirred.

'I'm wishing for him,' she said. Then she shut her eyes. 'Please, pudding, this is terribly important. Wag wishes I may never have to leave him again.'

Christmas has a queer way of seeming weeks away one minute and is almost there the next. This, of course, happened that Christmas. One reason why Christmas sneaked up on them so fast was that the children were so busy. Sebastian working with Mr Beaumont. Myra and Wolfgang were at the studio right up to Christmas Eve. The only one free was Ethel for her school broke up well before

Christmas so that the dancing staff could take those children appearing in plays and pantomimes to their rehearsals or to the theatre.

However, somehow all the shopping was done. Boxes of decorations and Christmas tree ornaments were piled in the schoolroom. In the larder there were nuts, raisins, crystallised fruits, sweets, in fact, everything that should be on a table on Christmas Day except crackers, which they could not have because bangs would frighten Wag and spoil his Christmas.

The day before Christmas Eve Mr Oslip finished filming early and there was a studio party. An enormous Christmas tree was pushed on to the floor with presents for everybody on it. Wolfgang was given a toy theatre with a curtain that came up and down, and whole sets of coloured scenery which only needed to be cut out. Myra was given a book about how to look after poodles. Wolfgang and Myra together gave Mr Oslip a little animal they had bought in Hong Kong. For the Production Manager, the floor manager, the continuity girl and all the electricians and cameramen they had pencils with their names on. Everybody was very pleased. They said pencils were a smashing present, especially with names on.

Christmas Eve was a mad rush. Last minute shopping. Last minute doing-up of parcels. Last minute decorations. Then at six o'clock David said:

'Come into the living-room, everybody. It's lighting-up time.'

Polly had decorated the tree. She had sprayed glittering frost all over it. She had hung glass icicles from the tips of

the branches. She had used mostly blue and purple ornaments and masses of tiny blue lights. On the top blazed a
large silvered Star of Bethlehem. It was beautiful.

'Makes you feel you ought to be kneelin' down, don't it?'
said Mrs Bottle.

Mumsmum, who with Mumsdad had come over for the
lighting up, gave Polly a kiss.

'Sometimes I doubt it, darling, but when I look at that
tree I know I've got a clever daughter.'

David's wish came completely true. It was a perfect
Christmas, from the early morning opening of bulging
stockings to the lovely playing of old carols by David and
Sebastian before bedtime.

But Boxing Day was terrible. Directly after breakfast,
while the children were sitting round the schoolroom table
writing thank-you letters, David broke the news to Polly.
Poor Polly was dreadfully upset. She had been miserable
enough in Los Angeles without the children, though she
knew they were having a lovely time in Devonshire. But
knowing they were left behind just for a film would be
heartbreaking.

David said that for Sebastian's next tour he was engaging
Paul to travel with them, and didn't Polly think she could
trust Sebastian to be safe with the two of them? Then she
could stay at home to be with the other three.

That made Polly more miserable.

'What an awful question! I'll be desperately unhappy
whichever I choose. I can't bear to think of months without
you. I'd loathe Sebastian to go on tour without me, but then
I detest the idea of leaving the other three behind.'

Polly's being miserable swept through the house until everybody, except Paul, was feeling unhappy too. Paul struggled to be part of the family gloom but he couldn't, he kept breaking out into gay whistling because he was going abroad.

'Sorry,' he said to Myra. 'It's not that I'm heartless. But going abroad is my Christmas pudding wish coming true.'

The one who suffered most from Polly being unhappy was Ethel. The day after Boxing Day Wolfgang had to be back at the studio so that meant Myra and Miss Popple went back too. Sebastian was either working at home, or Paul took him to lessons with Mr Beaumont, whom Sebastian liked very much indeed. But Ethel had three weeks' holiday and so she had to be at home. The plan had been that she would do lots of exciting things with her mother, including seeing those pantomimes in which pupils from the school were appearing. They did the exciting things but Polly, though she tried desperately hard to pretend she was not, was so miserable the things they did were not so much fun as they ought to have been.

So one morning Ethel decided she was tired of miserableness, so she told Miss Popple she had to go to school for a class. Miss Popple believed her and ordered the car.

School, Ethel found, looked odd in the holidays. No bells rang and there were no masses of running feet. But in the far distance she heard a piano playing so she went to see what was going on.

All the classrooms had glass panes in the doors. The piano was playing in the big dance classroom, so Ethel stood on tiptoe and peered in. A girl called Cora, whom she knew by sight, was dancing very badly on her pointes. Miss Carrot was teaching her.

'Look, dear,' Miss Carrot was saying, 'when they sing "Fairy folk come tripping" – play that again, will you, Miss Fortesque? – you trip in like this.'

Miss Fortesque, though she did not stop reading her paper, played the bars again and Miss Carrot showed how a fairy tripped.

'Now again,' Miss Carrot said. 'And let me see you do it, Cora.'

Cora was so bad that Ethel was shocked. Wag would do it better, she thought.

Miss Carrot sounded as though she was holding back being cross.

'You have to go on this afternoon, Cora. You can surely do better than that.'

Cora's face turned red and she sniffed, trying not to cry.

'I never did like ballet, Miss Carrot. I'll be all right in the other numbers.'

Miss Carrot tried to sound believing.

'I'm sure you will, dear, I'm sure you'll be splendid in the tap number. There was no thought of you being one of the eight fairies when you were engaged as understudy, but this measles has wrecked our plans.' She broke off, staring at Ethel's face pressed against the glass. She came over and opened the door. 'What are you doing here, Ettie?'

Ethel came in.

'Watching. Can I stay a little while? Myra and Wolf are at the studio, and Sebastian is having a lesson. I wish the term would start again.'

Miss Carrot barred the way.

'Have you had measles? We're having trouble with the *Cinderella* children, three down with measles.'

The Forums had all had measles, whooping cough and chicken-pox. Measles at Apple Bough, whooping cough in America and chicken-pox, without knowing it until Myra had it badly, while they were touring Australia, so Ethel was able to answer truthfully 'Yes,' so she came in and sat down.

'Mummy and I saw *Cinderella*,' she said to Cora. 'But you weren't there.'

Cora knew Ethel by sight because of her going to Madame's special ballet class.

'I've only understudied up till now. I'm never going to do this fairy stuff. I hate ballet.'

Miss Carrot was not having that.

'Now don't talk nonsense, dear. Academy students keep their chins up. Where there's a will there's a way. You wait until you are wearing Viola's pretty blue fairy dress, you'll feel quite different.'

'I won't,' said Cora. 'It's too short and too tight.'

Miss Carrot could have hit Cora. But she still spoke in a bright voice.

'Nonsense! Nonsense! Now again.'

Ethel felt sorry for Cora. She knew the steps but she had never tried to work at ballet, so her tail stuck out and her knees were bent and her ankles wobbled.

'Well, dear,' Miss Carrot said at last, still trying to sound bright, 'that's all we can do for now, we must have some lunch before we go to the theatre. What about you, Ettie? Who's calling for you?'

Ethel had arranged that the car would fetch her, but an idea was coming to her.

'Nobody until teatime.' She looked pleadingly at Miss Carrot – and Ethel could look very pleading when she tried. 'Could I come with you to the theatre? You see, there's nobody at home.'

Miss Carrot made tching-tching sounds. She usually had fourteen children, which included two understudies, to look after in the theatre. But today there would be only thirteen as Cora was going on for Viola, so Ethel would not be noticed. She was a favourite of Madame's and it seemed mean to send the child home to an empty house.

'All right. But you'll have to telephone to arrange to be fetched from the theatre.'

'I'll ring now,' Ethel said. 'I'll ask Paul – he's Sebastian's tutor – to fetch me.'

Ethel was competent with a telephone book. She found Mr Beaumont's number and asked for Paul.

'What's up?' he asked when he came to the phone.

'Could you do two things for me?' Ethel asked. 'First tell Mummy I have to stay at school until after tea so I don't want the car. Second, will you fetch me at five from the stage door of the Frivolity Theatre?'

'Ettie!' Paul's voice was stern. 'What are you up to?'

'Most probably nothing. You know how pleased you are because your plum pudding wish is coming true? Well, I just might be making mine.'

Ethel went to the canteen where she found Cora eating cold pie – food, Cora told her, was always cold in the holidays. So Ethel bought some pie too, and sat down next to her.

Cora was still sniffing.

'It's terrible about this measles. You see, they knew here how badly we need the money. Well, Dad's been in hospital and sick pay isn't much. So they got me this understudy in *Cinderella*, but only as one of the twelve, they all know I'm no good on my pointes, so I couldn't be a fairy. Now they're making me go on. I shouldn't wonder if there was a row. The stage manager's ever such a sarky type, I wouldn't put it past him to get me the sack.'

'It's only for today, isn't it? I mean, they're getting someone else?'

Cora nodded.

'Bringing Letty back from a tour of *Red Riding Hood*. She may be there by tonight, but it could be too late. Suppose I get a laugh when they see me as a fairy? The principal girl wouldn't half have it in for me. It's her big number.'

'Listen,' said Ethel. 'I've got an idea.' Then she began to whisper.

Ethel was so good and quiet in the dressing-room, and when she followed Miss Carrot on to the side of the stage while the dancing troupe were on the stage, that Miss Carrot almost forgot she was there. Because of this she did not notice when she and Cora disappeared behind a rail of stage costumes just before the fairy number. And thanks to the efforts of the other seven fairies she did not notice, and neither did her assistant, that it was Ethel who was dressed as the blue fairy and not Cora. In fact, she only noticed when the fairies were on the stage and then she nearly had hysterics. Ethel, though she had never worked on her pointes, was managing the dance splendidly. And with the help of elastic round the waist and several safety pins was not quite falling out of her dress. The shoes she and Cora had borrowed from someone's locker before they left the school.

'Who's the understudy? What a little charmer!' the stage manager whispered in Miss Carrot's ear.

Miss Carrot turned an anguished face to him.

'The naughty child! She's one of Madame's hopefuls but she's only nine.'

The stage manager whistled under his breath.

'Snatch her off the stage and out of the theatre directly the number finishes. If the L.C.C. are about I shall be hung, drawn and quartered.'

It was not truthfully a real ballet. Just some very simple steps while the principal girl sang, but to Ethel it was her plum pudding wish come true.

'I couldn't have enjoyed it more,' she told Paul when an indignant Miss Carrot had handed her over. 'It was gorgeous.'

Paul tried to sound disapproving.

'You're a bad girl. In England you mayn't put a foot on a stage until you're twelve and then you have to have a licence. No wonder that poor Miss Carrot was having the jitters.'

'Nobody saw, so nobody will ever know.'

Paul gave her shoulder an affectionate pat.

'You're a comic, young Ettie. But you make quite sure nobody ever does know or you'll be in trouble.'

Ettie was feeling prancy. She danced along beside Paul.

'I'm a fairy folk coming tripping. But don't fuss, I won't

tell anyone, not even the Bottles – except of course Myra, but telling her is like telling nobody – she's so safe.'

Paul laughed out loud.

'Thank goodness that's true of one of you.'

15

The Break-up

Almost up to the last minute Polly kept changing her mind. One day she was definitely staying at Number 10, the next she could not let Sebastian go on a tour with only David and Paul to look after him, she must go too. Then suddenly everything was settled. Miss Popple would be in charge of Number 10, though Mumsmum and Mumsdad would either call round or telephone every day. Polly would go on the Far East tour with Sebastian.

'I wonder what made Mummy decide at last,' Myra said to Sebastian.

He was in his bedroom putting things away that he was not taking with him on his tour.

'Me. I asked her to come with me.'

In Sebastian's room there was a table, so Myra sat in her favourite position, her arms folded, her chin resting on them.

'You! But you never do things like that.'

Sebastian came to the table.

'Mumsdad told me to. I'll tell you something else. He's buying this house with my money.'

Myra felt cold inside.

'Not with everything in it?'

'Yes. Mumsdad thought that would be best. Of course the Marshalls are taking some things away, but most are staying.' He looked in a pleased way round the bedroom. 'Everything in here is staying so what I'm putting away will be here when I come back, like you said.'

Myra could not make herself sound pleased.

'But it's such grand kind of furniture – not a bit like us.'

'Mumsdad says we can change what we don't like, but a house with furniture in it was the quickest way to have a home. He says decorating and furnishing takes ages.'

'I suppose it does,' Myra agreed. 'And I know Mumsdad and Mumsmum think this furniture awfully nice – and I suppose in a kind of everything-matching, fat-cushion way it is. Only it feels like the Marshalls, not us.'

Sebastian went back to putting his things away.

'I see that, but I shan't mind as much none of you being there now we have this house. Paul says he'll work out exactly what time it is in England, so we know what you're doing. It'll be like the Apple Bough remembering game.'

Myra looked at Sebastian's back and found it was beginning to swim for her eyes were full of tears. She got up and furtively brushed them away. How idiotic to cry when you got what you wanted, or at least part of what you wanted. But now they were coming up to departure day it was hard not to mind saying goodbye. In fact, hard not to mind being left behind, even when it was you who had planned to be left behind. Because she was ashamed of herself her voice was gruff.

'That game's no good to us for we won't know what you're doing. I suppose you'll write every week?'

Sebastian nodded.

'Of course.'

That was the last chance Myra and Sebastian had of talking to each other. There was so much to do, and, anyway, the studio took up most of Myra's day and what was over she usually spent doing things for Polly. On the day the family left, as the aeroplane did not take off until midday, Myra, Wolfgang and Ethel were out of the house first, which was a good thing for waving goodbye is not often a happy business. Instead there were quick hugs all round, then Myra and Wolfgang were in the studio car with Miss Popple, while Ethel was sitting beside the chauffeur in the family car. So, though there were a few tears, in the rush they did not last long.

The departure of the family for the Far East happened in the week when Mr Oslip first began shooting the scenes at Windsor Castle. The early scenes did not concern either Wolfgang or Myra, though the ballroom in which Eddie was to recite was already built and was most elegant looking, with a special chair for Queen Victoria on a little raised stage.

'I suppose I sit on the edge of that stage at Queen Victoria's feet,' Myra said to Miss Popple. Then she shuddered. 'Every time I think of it I feel cold inside.'

Miss Popple could understand that.

'I'm sure you do, dear, so would I. But it will be soon over, and think how much worse it would be if you had to say anything.'

'Don't!' said Myra. 'Even imagining it makes me feel sick.'

The next morning while they were at lessons in the schoolroom which had been built for them in the studio, George, the P.A., knocked at the door.

'Can you spare Myra for five minutes, Miss Popple? Mr Oslip wants her.'

Myra supposed that Mr Oslip wanted her because he was grouping his people in the ballroom, for he took a long time arranging a crowd. But when they found him he was sitting in his chair talking to the man who had written the film script.

'Hallo, Myra,' he said. 'Give her a chair, George. This is Mr Hiller.'

As Mr Hiller came to the shooting every day of course Myra knew him by sight, but she had never spoken to him before.

'How do you do? I'm Wolf's sister.'

Mr Hiller nodded.

'Look, we've come across a slight snag. Eddie had to learn a special poem to recite to Queen Victoria.'

Naturally Myra knew that, for Wolfgang was being coached in how to say it, and as he did not like the poem he came back cross from his coaching.

'I know. It's called "The Celestial Surgeon", it's by Robert Louis Stevenson.'

'It's fact,' Mr Hiller explained, 'that the boy did recite that poem, and the legend is that Queen Victoria wished to hear it. But somehow it doesn't sound like her choice. So we were

192

thinking of putting you in an earlier scene where you can ask your grandmother if the boy reciter might say it.'

It was lucky Myra was sitting or she might have fallen down. She fixed agonised eyes on Mr Oslip.

'You absolutely promised I said nothing.'

Mr Oslip was impatient of hold-ups in his film.

'This is almost nothing. All you have to say is: "Could he recite 'The Celestial Surgeon', Grandmama? It's my favourite."'

'That won't hurt you, will it?' Mr Hiller said. 'Let's hear you.'

Tremblingly Myra stood up. Then, looking extraordinarily like the pictures of Alice in Wonderland, she put her heels together, turned out her toes and said, by mistake, Wolfgang's name for the poem.

'Could he recite "The Detestable Surgeon", Grandmama? It's my favourite.'

Mr Oslip had looked upon Myra as a quiet, well-brought-up child, so he was surprised.

'Don't be silly, dear. We've no time to waste. Say it properly.'

But Myra couldn't. She tried hard but each time something was wrong. Either struggling not to say 'The Detestable' she stammered. Or she got her inflections wrong on 'It's my favourite.' First she emphasised 'It', then 'my' and finally 'favourite'. She was bitterly ashamed to be so stupid but she could not get it right. In the end she got everything wrong. She looked despairingly at Mr Oslip.

'I'm sorry. I am trying terribly hard.'

It was Mr Hiller who came to her rescue for he roared with laughter.

'If ever there was an unwilling actress it's you. Don't worry, dear. Somebody else shall say the line.'

Myra, describing what had happened to Miss Popple, said:

'I felt lower than a snake, Popps. I thought nobody could be as unimportant as I was, but imagine not being able to say one simple line! I shall never get over the humiliation.'

'What nonsense!' said Miss Popple briskly. 'The people here imagine everybody wishes to be an actress or actor. But there are plenty like you about whose gifts lie in other directions.'

Perhaps because she had nearly had to say a line and now had nothing to say Myra enjoyed being the Princess. It was curious, she found, how real things became when you were dressed up. She was, of course, still of no importance in the studio world, but in Windsor Castle ballroom she was the Queen's granddaughter, and treated as such. Queen Victoria was a great stickler for etiquette, and etiquette demanded that everybody who was not royal kept their place. So, though Wolfgang was a star boy reciter and the old Queen was very kind to him, it was to a commoner she was being kind, but when she smiled down at Myra it was to a member of her family.

'It was fun just for once,' Myra told Miss Popple, who was helping her out of her Princess dress, 'but I'm glad I'm not an actress. What a life!'

By the end of the month everything that Eddie, the boy, had to do was finished, for Edward, the man, was taking over. Wolfgang had not decided exactly how Mr Oslip would say goodbye, but he had supposed it would be rather like the party at Christmas. But Mr Oslip was thinking of nothing but the shots he was shooting the next day. So when Wolfgang came to him to say goodbye he was surprised.

'Of course you've finished, haven't you? I'll look out for you at the trade show of the picture.'

Wolfgang did not say so but inside he was livid. What a way to treat a star!

'How wonderful,' said Miss Popple as she got into the car, 'to think that's all over! It's been a pleasant experience, but I shall be glad when we're back in our own schoolroom.'

'Speak for yourself, Popps,' Wolfgang growled. 'I'm never glad to be in a schoolroom.'

That was the beginning of an unhappy time at Number 10. Wolfgang missed the studio life generally, and showed how much he was missing it by being what Mrs Bottle called 'a proper termigant'. It was not altogether Wolfgang's fault; he had always had someone to do things with at the studio, for if there were no other boys about there was Tom, the stand-in. If only Paul had been there he would have understood and found ways to get the black dog off Wolfgang's shoulder. But as there was no Paul, Wolfgang made life horrible for Myra and Miss Popple, though in between he was sorry.

'I can't seem to help it, Popps. I've got used to a public life and I'm abhorring a private one.'

It did not help that now there was no studio to go to, there was time for both Myra and Wolfgang to notice how dreadfully they were missing David and Polly.

'I do hope I didn't make a mistake about a home,' Myra confided to Miss Popple. 'I hadn't known how un-home-ish a house would be without a father and mother in it.'

Miss Popple was not feeling too happy about things either but she was not going to tell Myra so.

'Of course, you didn't. The great thing is that you have a home. I feel it in my bones that everything is going to work out splendidly.'

'I hope you're right,' Myra said. 'Just now I'd say the only one of us who was fairly happy was Ettie and, of course, Wag.'

Then suddenly things improved. It was just after Wolfgang was twelve, when one morning the film studio rang up. It was the head secretary from the department which looked after artists under contract. She asked to speak to Miss Popple.

'Would you take Wolfie to the County Hall for a licence? There's a serial coming on TV and he's being considered for the part of the boy.'

It was no good telling Wolfgang he was only being considered. It was as if an outward shell fell off him and out came the ordinary Wolfgang nobody had seen since the film finished. The first thing he did was to rush out to the kitchen.

'Mrs Bottle – Mr Bottle – I'm going on telly.'

Of course the Bottles were as thrilled as Wolfgang.

'That's ever so nice, dear,' Mrs Bottle said. 'And just the right place for you, I shouldn't wonder.'

Mr Bottle dug Wolfgang in the chest with one finger.

'And while you're there you might 'ave a word with any 'igh-ups you meet to tell 'em we don't want no more talks nor brains' trusts.'

Wolfgang got his licence with no trouble at all. He was good at lessons so he could answer the questions put to him, and though he was small he was strong. Two days later Miss Popple took him to the television studios to be seen by the producer of the serial. Myra went too as a matter of course, for Miss Popple always took the two of them out in the afternoons. Wag, very cross at missing his walk, stayed at home with the Bottles.

Ever since Sebastian had left on his tour there had been no car or chauffeur. Ethel was usually driven to school by Mumsmum, though sometimes Miss Popple took her. When they had to go far they travelled by what is called 'usual means of transport' which means buses and Undergrounds. That day they went all the way to the TV studio on a bus, and since you can't time buses like you can a private car they arrived too soon. This meant they had to hang about outside, which, as Myra said to Miss Popple afterwards, would have made anyone but Wolfgang nervous. Wolfgang was, of course, not nervous at all and walked into the producer's office looking as calm as if he was walking into his own bedroom.

The producer, called Mr Brown, was a nice-looking young man with horn-rimmed glasses. His eyes twinkled as he looked at Wolfgang.

'I've seen some stills of you in your film, but you've had your hair cut.'

'Would I need it long in your serial?'

'Longer than it is now. Did you ever read a book called *Holiday House?*'

Wolfgang looked at Myra.

'We haven't had that, have we?'

Myra was going to say no when Miss Popple said:

'*Holiday House!* My brother and I had it when we were children. I think we still have the book somewhere.'

Mr Brown turned to her.

'I was thinking of Wolf as Harry. Don't you think there's a resemblance?'

Miss Popple laughed.

'I don't remember the book well, but I do seem to remember Harry and Laura were always in trouble.'

'They certainly were,' Mr Brown agreed. He fetched a script from his desk. 'Read a bit of this, Wolf, starting here.'

The scene was a conversation between Harry and Laura, during which they decided to give a party. Their grandmother, with whom they lived, was away because she was ill, so Harry and Laura, without telling anybody, wrote out the invitations and sent them by hand to all their friends.

Then Mr Brown told Wolfgang to skip a couple of pages to where Mrs Crabtree, the children's nurse, heard of the party. Mr Brown read Mrs Crabtree's part, and very fierce he sounded.

'I never heard of such doings in all my life, Master Harry.'

'But, Mrs Crabtree, please ... '

'Don't you please me, Master Harry.'

'But, Mrs Crabtree ... '

'As sure as eggs are eggs you shall repent for this, for not one morsel of cake ... '

'No cake!'

'Or anything else shall you have to give any of the party: no, not so much as a crust of bread or a thimbleful of tea.'

'Then what are they to eat?'

'No more than you have every night for your suppers – two biscuits and two cups of milk.'

Wolfgang was enthralled.

'Is that all they had?' he asked.

'That was all, and though their relations gave a wonderful party afterwards the children never lived that bad party down.'

'What else does Harry do?'

'Sets a bedroom on fire. Saves Laura from a mad bull. Has to escape from a locked room by dropping from the window into a gardener's arms, and helps decorate the house to celebrate the winning of the Battle of Waterloo.'

'Wasn't there a tragic end?' Miss Popple asked. 'I seem to remember crying ovef it.'

Mr Brown nodded.

'There was indeed. Poor Frank, the elder brother, takes pages to die. But I'm not using any of that in my adaptation; for one thing it happened when Harry and Laura were older. Actually, I switch things round so that the Waterloo illuminations and fireworks, plus a fight for Harry with a pickpocket, finishes the serial.'

'When do we start?' Wolfgang asked.

That led to a business discussion between Miss Popple and Mr Brown about times of rehearsals and outside filming dates. Then Mr Brown said:

'I take it you will be Wolf's chaperon, Miss Popple?'

'Of course,' Miss Popple agreed. 'His mother would not allow anyone else to look after him. But Myra would have to come too, is that all right?'

Mr Brown smiled at Myra.

'Of course. I shall want a lot of children in the bad party scene. I expect I could use you.'

As soon as they were home Wolfgang rushed out to the kitchen roaring out his news as he came, so Myra was alone in the living-room when Mumsdad came in.

'I take it,' he said, 'from the noise Wolfie's making that he's acting in the serial.'

'Yes.' Myra put her arm through his. 'Do you ever have mean thoughts, Mumsdad?'

'Often. Are you having some now?'

Myra looked up at him.

'I'm very pleased Wolf's on TV if that's what he wants. But, my goodness, I do wish sometimes it was me that was important. I know Popps had to ask if I could come to rehearsals, and I'm sure Mr Brown meant to be nice. But between them they made me feel like a parcel that has to be put down somewhere where it won't be in anyone's way. It's a miserable feeling.'

16

News

One day when Myra, Wolfgang, Miss Popple and Wag went to fetch Ethel from the Academy of Dancing and Stage Training she came flying out to meet them.

'It's happened! The letter about me has come.'

Ethel was always talking about the letter Madame Leninskya had promised to write, so they were not surprised.

'The one to Dame Ninette de Valois, I suppose,' Wolfgang said.

'Not exactly. It's the one to her but she's sent it for Madame Fidolia to add more about me.' She turned to Miss Popple. 'She said I was to ask you to come in to see her.'

Miss Popple looked like an agitated hen.

'Oh, dear! Am I looking tidy, Myra? That woman scares me.'

Miss Popple always looked tidy in a bulgy way, but Myra stroked back a small wisp of hair which had come out from under her hat.

'You look nice and Popplish.'

'I expect you ought to curtsy,' said Wolfgang.

Ethel took Miss Popple by the hand.

'Come on, Popps. Of course you don't curtsy, Wolf's being silly.'

Madame Fidolia was looking almost exactly as she had the first time Miss Popple had seen her. She was again wearing the black taffeta dress with short sleeves, and her pink tights and shoes, but this time her shawl was yellow. She greeted Miss Popple graciously.

'How do you do? Will you please sit down. You may leave us, Ettie. Get your things on ready to go home.'

Ethel swept one of her beautiful curtsies.

'Thank you, Madame.'

When the door had shut Madame leant across her desk.

'That is the most talented child I have taught since my great pupil, Posy Fossil.'

Miss Popple felt an answer was expected.

'That is nice, isn't it?'

Madame smiled.

'You do not, I imagine, know much about dancing, but you can take my word that this is true. There is, too, remarkable musicality.'

Miss Popple had during the past years heard that word almost every day, so she had learnt to accept that it was considered a good quality to have.

'That's nice, isn't it?' she said again.

'But naturellement,' Madame went on, as if Miss Popple had not spoken, 'nothing can be taken for granted with a dancer. So much can go wrong, nothing – nothing is certain.'

'I suppose that's true of everything.'

Again Madame did not seem to know Miss Popple had spoken.

'I am asking you to see me today because I feel – and this I wrote to my friend Leninskya in Paris – that the time is coming for Ettie to leave me. She has learnt much here, but this is not the training school for her. We are asking for an audition for her at The Royal Ballet School. If a date for this should be fixed will you arrange to take her?'

Miss Popple was sure nobody questioned Madame's plans but she had to explain about Wolfgang.

'But if I can't go with her, her grandmother will.'

Madame Fidolia gave an accepting little bow.

'That will be quite satisfactory. If my health permits I shall be there myself, but as a spectator, not in charge of the child.'

Miss Popple saw the interview was over.

'Shall I hear from you when the audition is to be?'

'Naturellement.' Madame Fidolia gave her a gracious, dismissing smile. 'Forgive that I do not get up but I am a little lame.'

To her surprise Miss Popple found her knees giving a small bend, as if they were trying to curtsy. My word, she thought as she walked to the front door, what with Mr Ruttenstein and that Madame we can't call our souls our own.

There were to be six episodes to *Holiday House*. Each would be given live on Saturdays in the Children's programme. The rehearsals would be each afternoon in the week, but on transmission day they would be working all day in the studio. But before they got to the rehearsals there was a lot of outside filming to be done. Also Harry had many clothes to be fitted, for the children in *Holiday House* were rich. Wolfgang was bored with the fittings but he found the filming fun, for the part of Laura was being played by a girl called Angela to whom he took an enormous fancy. Angela had been acting in films since she was four and had appeared twice on television. She was bad for Wolfgang for she despised all authority, which made life tough for Mr Brown's staff and for her governess, Miss Sampson.

'What's your governess like?' she asked Wolfgang during the first day's filming. 'Mine's nice but she can't look after me. Whatever I do and however bad I am I see her thinking – "'I must make allowances for this clever child."'

Wolfgang felt he had been done out of something but he was not going to let Angela know.

'Yes, that's just how Popps thinks about me.'

Of course it did not take Angela a day to see that this was a lie, but she was glad of someone to do things with so she decided to train Wolfgang.

'There's no need to go running back to your governess as if you were a baby,' she told him. 'You do what I do. Directly they've finished shooting a scene follow me. When they want us again they shout for us through that loudspeaker.'

Two houses were used for the film shots and both had large grounds, ideal for Wolfgang and Angela to disappear in. But delightful as the grounds were Myra got tired of them for, as she discovered, even with the nicest dog, walks round grounds become a bore when you do them alone every day. Though it was nearly summer it was cold so she could not just sit and read a book. She watched Wolfgang and Angela balancing on the tops of walls, climbing ladders, giving each other rides in a wheelbarrow, and wished she could have found what they were doing fun, but she felt too old for that sort of thing, and, anyway, did not want to be seen playing with them, for she was certain one or the other would ruin the lovely early nineteenth-century clothes they wore. Sometimes they did tear them, but if they did the wardrobe staff were there to stitch them together again, and Angela did not care how much trouble she gave, and Wolfgang was learning not to. Each day Miss Popple and Angela's governess, Miss Sampson, tried to get hold of them to keep them quiet but, as Miss Sampson knew, it was a waste of time, for the moment a shot was over Angela had grabbed Wolfgang's hand and they were off.

Myra did have one day's work when, dressed in party clothes, she, and some other children, drove up to the door of one of the houses they were using and was seen being let in by a disapproving butler. But mostly she was bored – bored – bored.

The outdoor shooting was nearly over before Ethel was called to her audition. The letter came to Madame Fidolia. Ethel Forum, it said, was to be at Colet Gardens, where the senior dancing students were trained, at eleven o'clock next Tuesday.

Because she thought it would make a change Myra asked Miss Popple if she might go to the audition.

'Of course, dear. It will be very nice for Ettie to have you.'

'It's not for Ettie,' Myra admitted. 'It's to get away from that boring filming.'

That worried Miss Popple.

'I was afraid you were bored, dear, but, if Miss Sampson's right, it will be worse when rehearsals start. It's not so bad for me, Miss Sampson's had an interesting time with Angela, she's travelled nearly as much as we have. But at least rehearsals will be indoors so I can set you some work to do.'

Mumsmum, who drove them to Ethel's audition, was in what she called a 'twit'.

'It's an exciting occasion for me. I've not been to an audition since the first time I sang for our local operatic society. I got only a small part that time, but the next year I had the lead. I was a slim little thing with a lovely soprano voice.'

Myra looked thoughtfully at Mumsmum's sofa-ish figure. She wished she had not said that about being a slim little thing. It was undignified somehow, especially as she was quite perfect as she was.

There were a lot of children at the audition. Most of them, like Ethel, changed into tunics, but one wore a tutu, and several wore their ordinary clothes. Most of them had their Mums with them and most of the Mums talked about their children.

'My Phyllis is a lovely little dancer,' one Mum told Mumsmum. 'The mayor said only last week she ought to be given a decoration for she's earned so much for charity.'

Another Mum, combing her child's curls, said to everybody:

'I suppose you all recognise Margaret. She's the little dancer in the advert on telly for that peppermintado.'

'I don't think they'll like that here,' a third Mum whispered to Myra. 'Very exclusive they are. My Joanna's teacher says she's just the type.'

Myra looked at Ethel who, uninterested in anyone else, was limbering up in a corner of the room.

'I think that's what my sister's teacher – that's my sister over there – thinks about her.'

The mother looked appraisingly at Ethel.

'Where'd she learn?' Myra told her. Joanna's Mum shook her head. 'I wouldn't hope too much, dear, if I was you. I'd say stage school pupils were out.'

A young teacher came in, she had a list of names.

'Good morning. Will you answer to your names?' Ethel's name came last but, to the surprise of the Mums, she was auditioned first. 'Come along, dear,' said the teacher, holding out a hand to her. 'Madame Fidolia felt well enough to come, but we don't want to keep her hanging about.'

Ethel had never doubted Madame Fidolia had been a great dancer, but that morning at Colet Gardens she had proof. The old lady was treated like a Queen. She had dressed for the occasion, so for the first time Ethel saw her in almost ordinary clothes. That is to say, a wide taffeta skirt, a short green silk coat, proper shoes and silk stockings, but she still wore no hat. She was sitting beside the Director, looking as regal as usual but very much at home. Ethel swept a beautiful curtsy, including as many people in it as she could.

'This is Ettie Forum,' Madame Fidolia said. 'I would like you to see what she can do.'

It was very like the first time Ethel had danced for Madame Fidolia except there was no music. First she did some exercises at the barre. Then a set of steps in the centre, but before she was asked to take off her socks the Director asked Madame Fidolia if she had anything special she would like them to see Ethel do. Madame nodded and directed Ethel to do some of her special jumps. Then Ethel took off her shoes and socks.

There was a lot of whispering after that before Madame Fidolia said: 'That is all, dear,' and someone called: 'We are ready for the next, please.'

Outside Myra said:

'What happened? Will they have you?'

Mumsmum unlocked the car.

'I was disappointed. I'd hoped to come in and look at them all.'

But Ethel was too much in a dream to answer. Instead she spoke what she was thinking out loud.

'When I'm as old as Madame Fidolia, that's how other great dancers are going to look at me.'

'Were they so very polite to her?' Myra asked.

'Polite!' Ethel struggled for words to explain. 'They put on faces like Sir Walter Raleigh laying down his cloak for Queen Elizabeth. And I just knew that one day it was going to happen to me.'

Mumsmum started the car.

'I know that is how you've been brought up,' she said briskly, 'but when I was young I'd have been told pride comes before a fall, Ettie.'

Ethel, as everybody had expected including herself, was accepted by The Royal Ballet School. Wolfgang, as again everybody including himself had expected, was a great success as Harry, but Myra was more disappointed with herself every day, and the more disappointed with herself she felt the harder it was to talk to anybody about it. She would have talked to Sebastian but he was staying on in San Francisco to have lessons with Misken. She would have liked to have talked to Grandfather, but they could not go to Devonshire until Wolfgang's serial ended at the end of August. She might have talked to Miss Popple only she felt she might worry her. Of course there were the Bottles, but fond as she was of them they could not be expected to understand, so she fell back on Wag.

'I know Grandfather said a talent could be for wisdom and being a good sister, but quite truthfully, Wag, neither Wolf nor Ettie need me like they used to, they are quite happy as they are. The awful thing is I ought to be too. I wanted a home, and here it is, beautifully furnished if you like this sort of Marshall furniture, only you and I don't. I don't know if it's my age – fourteen is difficult, almost grown-up but not quite. If it's not my age it must be I'm jealous. It's no good looking up at me with that loving face, it could be that I'm jealous. It's not easy to be the eldest of a family of which the rest are Sebastian, Wolf and Ettie. You ought to try it and you'd see. It's not that I want to do any of the things they do, but it's awful to feel permanently inferior. I expect Grandfather will help to make me understand, only September is a long way off and I wouldn't be surprised if I had an incurable inferiority complex before then. Imagine having to tell Grandfather all this, own up that in spite of all I said about wanting a home, now I've got it I'm absolutely miserable.'

But Myra did not get a chance to confess to Grandfather. For, a week before they left for Devonshire, something happened.

Myra had a bit of a cold so she had not gone to the Social Club used by television as a rehearsal room, but had stayed at home with Wag and the Bottles. As soon as Miss Popple, Wolfgang and Ethel, who often went to rehearsals in the holidays, had left, Mrs Bottle came bustling out from the kitchen with a hot water-bottle.

'You 'ave a nice lie down, dear. Like enough you'll drop off. I'll wake you when it's teatime.'

'But I'm not a bit sleepy, only stuffy,' Myra protested.

Mrs Bottle put an arm round her and led her towards the stairs.

'Then 'ave a nice read. Nothing like a lie down for a cold.'

So Myra took *The Secret Garden* to bed, meaning to reread it, but soon, just what Mrs Bottle had supposed would happen did. She was asleep and so was Wag.

They woke to find Mrs Bottle shaking Myra.

'Sorry to wake you, dear. But an old man brought this.' She held out a cable. 'It's for Miss Popple. Did we ought to ring up that place where Wolfie's re'earsing? It might be important.'

Mr Ruttenstein was a great man for cables so all the Forums were used to them.

'I'll open it,' said Myra. 'If it's urgent I'll read it to Popps on the phone.' Casually she opened the cable, read it, then, turning a sickly green, let it drop on to the bed.

Mrs Bottle picked it up.

'Sebastian ill,' she read. 'Returning immediately. Love to the children. Forum.'

17

The Amati

Mrs Bottle, with great sense, rang up Mumsdad and told him what was in the cable.

'And young Myra as near as makes no difference fainted dead away so, although it's addressed to Miss Popple, I didn't see, nor did Bottle, it was much good telling 'er, seeing she 'as to stay where she is until the re'earsal's over.'

Mumsdad said Mrs Bottle was quite right and he and Mumsmum would be round right away. But inside he was furious.

'Idiotic cable to send,' he growled to Mumsmum. 'We don't know whether David or Polly worded it, but they should have known one of the children might open it. I don't suppose there's much wrong or they wouldn't bring Sebastian all this way, but why not say what's the matter?'

He was even crosser when he saw Myra.

'Don't look like that, darling,' he said, giving her a kiss. 'You're the colour of a cabbage. I'll put a call through right away and see what is wrong.'

'But it's only half-past eight in the morning there,' said Myra. 'They mightn't be up yet.'

Mumsdad looked tough.

'I don't care what time it is. I hope I get them out of bed, it will teach them not to send frightening cables.'

Mumsdad was quite right, the cable was more frightening than the facts. He had got Polly on the phone. He called Myra to speak to her when he had finished, but there was no time for more than an ecstatic 'Mummy!' from Myra and an equally ecstatic 'Darling!' from Polly before Mumsdad put down the receiver.

'No good wasting pounds on coo-ing at each other, they'll be home tomorrow.'

'What's the matter with Sebastian?' Mumsmum asked.

They were having tea in the living-room, so Mumsdad led the way back there before he answered.

'He hasn't been well for two or three weeks. Now the doctor has decided it's a grumbling appendix so, since it's no good to him, it's to come out.'

Mumsmum poured out more tea for them all.

'But why bring him back here?'

'Sebastian refused to have his appendix out unless he could come.' Mumsdad jabbed a finger in the direction of Myra. 'I gather he said he would like to have you around.'

Like the sky turning pink at sunset, colour came back into Myra's face while something that, though it was nice, hurt, happened inside her.

'To be with me?'

That amused Mumsmum.

'Does that surprise you? I've often said I didn't know what the others would do without you.'

Myra felt embarrassed so she pretended to be busy folding a piece of bread and butter for Wag.

'I wasn't sure. I know it was like that once, but now they're all busy with their own things.'

Mumsdad got up. As he passed Myra's chair he ran his fingers through her hair.

'You have a trouble which is unique in your family. You underestimate yourself.'

The next day the family and Paul came home. At least David, Polly and Paul came to Number 10. Sebastian was taken straight to a nursing home. That evening Myra was allowed to visit him.

It was not really long since they had seen each other but, in spite of letters, there was a lot to catch up on. What new music Sebastian had been working on with Misken. Whether the concerto had said anything different when he played it again. What Paul was like on tour. That made Sebastian laugh.

'I was sick last week and Mummy flapped, but Paul said: "Now, don't get in a state, Mrs F. Better out than in, as Mrs Bottle would say."'

'She does,' Myra agreed. 'I was a little sick after the cable came about you, and that's exactly what she said.'

'I don't know why you were, an appendix is nothing. I'll be home in ten days.'

Myra explained about the wording of the cable.

'It was all right after Mumsdad talked to Mummy on the telephone. Has Mr Ruttenstein had to cancel any of your concerts?'

Sebastian, who had been looking well because he was seeing Myra, suddenly looked tired.

'Not yet. He's over here now about that.'

'Over here! He might have let you have your appendix out without him.'

'He's staying at The Savoy. I don't think it's all to do with me. I've got that tour of Russia in October. I don't want to cancel that, Myra, I think he'd be cross.'

'Does anyone think you need?'

'I shouldn't think so, but you know how people fuss. I saw him after the Misken concert and do you know what he said? "I want to hear you play that on the Amati."'

Myra hugged herself.

'How gorgeous! It does sound as if he was giving it you soon.'

Sebastian nodded.

'After the next tour I wouldn't wonder.'

A nurse came in.

'Sorry I've got to turn you out. Sebastian's had a long day. But you can see him tomorrow.'

But Myra did not see Sebastian the next day, for he had a little pain in the night and the doctor decided it was a mistake to keep him hanging about, so before lunch the next day his appendix was gone.

Naturally the children knew that Sebastian was famous, but he had to have his appendix out to bring home to them how famous he was. The evening papers had posters saying: 'Sebastian Forum ill.' The nursing home received so many flowers for him they ran out of space to put down the vases, so they arranged the overflow outside in the passage. The telephone never stopped ringing. Cables arrived from all over the world, and no one could go outside Number 10 without being stopped to be asked, 'What's the news?' The bell rang so often that at last Mrs Bottle said:

'Better pretend 'e's royal and stick somethin' on the gate.'

So Miss Popple wrote on a card:

'Sebastian's condition is very satisfactory.'

The cause of all this fuss was propped up in bed feeling drowsy and contented, allowed only to be peeped at by David and Polly. But the next day David was allowed a short proper visit. He drew up a chair and read Sebastian some of his nicest cables. Then he said:

'Your surgeon doesn't like too many visitors so Mummy's coming tomorrow. I came today because I've been making plans. How would you like six weeks in Devonshire?'

'I couldn't stay six weeks,' Sebastian answered sleepily. 'We said we'd be in Moscow before that.'

David patted the lump under the bedclothes where Sebastian's knees were.

'That's off, old man. You've done enough touring for the time being. I'm seeing Mr Ruttenstein this evening to suggest, if all goes well, he might be able to fit Russia in next year. They're pleased with you but they seem to think a rest wouldn't hurt you. So I thought Devonshire for six weeks and then Number 10 until Christmas. How's that?'

Sebastian was very sleepy or he would have protested then, but David almost at once started to tell him of Mrs Bottle's disbelief in nursing-home cooking, and how she was planning to bring his meals to him. Then the nurse came in and said that time was up.

ong time after David had gone Sebastian still did
in what he had heard. He lay drowsily trying to
trace a design on the curtain. It was not, in fact, until the
nurses came in to make his bed that he seemed to jerk
awake and realise what his father had said.

'Can I have a telephone, please?' he asked his own nurse.

She had taken a great fancy to Sebastian, but he was so
small she found it hard to believe he was thirteen.

'Not today, dear, perhaps tomorrow. We'll see.'

Sebastian looked despairingly at the two bent figures
tucking in, folding and smoothing.

'It's very important.'

But in his nurse's view the only thing that was important
for a small boy's recovery from an appendicitis operation
was sleep and food, so she missed the note of urgency in
Sebastian's voice.

'Don't you worry about telephones tonight. I expect you
can ring up anyone you like in the morning.'

Alone, Sebastian fought a losing battle for control of
himself. Tonight Daddy was talking to Mr Ruttenstein.
Tonight Mr Ruttenstein was hearing the autumn tour was
off. At that very minute perhaps. Mr Ruttenstein wouldn't
say he was angry, but he would be. He could be so angry that
he sold the Amati or gave it away to someone else.

If Sebastian had been himself he would have kept his
head, rung the bell and asked someone to send a message to
his father. But nobody is quite themselves the day after their
appendix is taken out. So Sebastian worried and worried,
and as he worried he grew hotter and hotter until he felt as
if he was boiling inside but had no way to let the steam out.

Presently his nurse came in to say good night before she went off duty. She looked at Sebastian, stroked his forehead then, as if she saw nothing wrong, said:

'It's time you were asleep.' Then she walked quietly out to ask the floor sister to send for Sebastian's doctor.

An hour later the news reached Number 10 that Sebastian was not so well.

All night, in spite of sleeping-pills, Sebastian had terrible dreams in which he was rushing round a concert hall chasing the Amati. The Amati wanted to be caught as much as he wanted to catch it, so as it ran it sobbed in its exquisite voice: 'Se-bas-ti-an – Se-bas-ti-an. Help me. Se-bas-ti-an.'

In the morning every newspaper told a shocked world that young Sebastian Forum was very ill indeed. The man who read the news on the wireless said: 'The child's condition is giving rise to anxiety.'

Myra did not know Sebastian was worse until she came down in the morning to give Wag his first 'out'. On the way she looked in at the kitchen to say good morning to the Bottles. As she opened the door she heard Mrs Bottle sobbing and heard Mr Bottle say:

'Don't take on, dear. Sebastian will be all right, you mark my words. You know what kids are – alarmin' ill one minute and right as rain the next.'

Mrs Bottle found it difficult to be heard between her sobs.

'They don't say on the wireless 'is condition is giving rise to anxiety, unless they're expecting 'im to die.'

Myra felt as if she was turning into an icicle.

'Did they say that about Sebastian?'

'Oh, my word!' said Mrs Bottle, mopping her eyes. 'I never

'eard you come in, young Myra, but you may as well learn the truth first as last. Yes, dear, 'e's took a turn for the worse. Cruel bad, 'e is.'

Myra, because it was something she did every day, took Wag into the garden. But she had no idea they were there. She stared unseeingly at Mr Bottle's late roses. Sebastian going to die! But people didn't who only had their appendix out. Besides, Daddy had said yesterday they were pleased with him. Then she remembered something. It was something she had only half heard, about Devonshire and coming back here afterwards. It was something Daddy had said to Miss Popple and she had supposed it was about herself, Wolfgang and Ethel. But suppose it was about Sebastian and Daddy had told him? Myra called Wag and went into the house.

David and Polly had scarcely slept and were on their way to the nursing home. They knew it was not likely that they could see Sebastian, but they could not bear not to be near him. Myra caught David's arm.

'Daddy, when you saw Sebastian did you say he was going to Devonshire?'

Polly gave her a kiss.

'Don't worry Daddy now, darling, and try not to worry yourself. The doctor says this temperature which is so frightening could go down as quickly as it went up.'

Myra gently pulled herself away from Polly.

'Did you tell him about Devonshire, Daddy?'

David struggled to attend to Myra.

'He was fine then. Yes, I told him I thought we'd have some weeks in Devonshire – and then come back here . . . '

It was not like David to break down. Almost crossly he took Polly's arm. 'Come on, darling,' and he ran her out of the house to the waiting taxi.

Myra went into the schoolroom where Miss Popple and Paul were trying to pretend to Wolfgang and Ethel that they were eating breakfast.

'Ah, there you are, dear!' said Miss Popple. 'I'll pour you out some coffee.'

Wolfgang looked up from the cereal he was eating.

'Sebastian's so ill it was on the wireless.'

'I'd say that was fame,' said Ethel.

Myra handed Wag's lead to Wolfgang.

'Take him out when you go. I've got something I've got to do.'

'Not before your breakfast,' said Miss Popple.

Myra did not answer but went up to her room and put on the best of her coats and a pair of gloves. Then she crept down the stairs. In the hall Paul was waiting.

'If you'd thoughts of seeing Sebastian it's no good, Myra. They wouldn't let you in.'

'I hadn't.' Suddenly she remembered something. 'Have you got any money you could lend me? Enough for a rather expensive taxi?'

Paul put his arm through hers.

'Heaps. But we'll travel together. What's the address, lady?'

'The Savoy,' said Myra.

At The Savoy the hall porter said Mr Ruttenstein had left a message to say he was not to be disturbed until he rang, but after a few words from Paul on the telephone a page-boy showed Myra up.

Mr Ruttenstein had put on his dressing-gown but had got back into bed. He stared at Myra as if he were afraid of her. She, of course, knew him but she did not suppose he knew her by sight.

'I'm Myra Forum, Sebastian's eldest sister.'

'Of course.' Mr Ruttenstein pointed to a chair. 'Sit down. Have they sent you to tell me some bad news?'

'No, nobody sent me. I came on my own. You see, I think I know why Sebastian's worse, and it's to do with you.'

'Had any breakfast?' Mr Ruttenstein asked.

'No, but I don't feel eat-ish.'

Mr Ruttenstein picked up a telephone and barked 'Service' into it. Then he said:

'Neither do I. But starving won't help Sebastian.'

When the waiter came he ordered coffee, toast and butter and orange juice. Then he settled himself back against his pillows.

'Let's have it. How am I responsible for Sebastian's relapse?'

'It's not you really, it was Daddy. You see, yesterday he told him he'd go to Devonshire and then come back to London.'

'That's perfectly correct. That is what your father told me.'

'But don't you see, that would mean Sebastian would miss his autumn concerts.'

'He certainly will.'

Myra wished the breakfast would come. Mr Ruttenstein might be brighter after a cup of coffee.

'Can't you see how awful that was for Sebastian?'

Mr Ruttenstein didn't find looking kind easy, but he tried.

'It's disappointing, but these things will happen.'

Myra clasped her hands.

'I suppose you've never known what it's meant to Sebastian. To have it he'd have played and played just as long as you said he was to.' Myra felt she was going to cry and she must not until she had finished telling him. She held her throat and swallowed hard. 'Don't put off the concerts. It's thinking you're angry because he can't play at them that's making him so ill. It's sort of losing hope.' It was too difficult. Tears poured down her cheeks.

Mr Ruttenstein passed Myra a silk handkerchief.

'There's a bathroom through there. Go wash your face and maybe the coffee will have come.'

When Myra came out of the bathroom, rather smeared looking and still crying a little, the breakfast had arrived. Mr Ruttenstein handed her a cup of coffee.

'Tell me, Myra, what is this "it" that I have never understood what it has meant to Sebastian?'

Myra nearly dropped her cup.

'The Amati, of course.'

Mr Ruttenstein shook his head.

'Maybe I'm dense. But what has my Amati got to do with the cancelled concerts?'

Myra could not believe the great Mr Ruttenstein could be so stupid.

'You know without my telling you. You told Sebastian that if he played at every concert until you told him he could stop you would give him your Amati. He knows it's got to be now because you can't cash in on him so well when he's grown up.'

Mr Ruttenstein leant forward and gave the breakfast table such a thump everything on it jumped.

'Who told you this nonsense?'

'Sebastian.'

Mr Ruttenstein looked as though he was going to be sick.

'Sebastian believed that I was bribing him that way?'

'Yes.'

Mr Ruttenstein slapped his forehead.

'Listen, Myra. Your brother is such a master when he's playing that sometimes I forget – we all do – that he's only a boy, and a small boy. When I told him he was to have my Amati I forgot. That's why he misunderstood.'

'What did you tell him?'

Mr Ruttenstein scowled as he tried to remember.

'You know about fiddles?' Myta nodded. 'Until now Sebastian has never played on a full-sized fiddle, he's been too small. So I said he'd have to wait for one year, or two ...'

'You said he was to do the tours you chose for him. He doesn't make things up.'

Mr Ruttenstein slapped his forehead again.

'Maybe I said if he was a good boy, or something like that. But there was no bribe, I was just waiting for him to be big enough. When I knew he was ill and that I was coming over I thought: "I think Sebastian will be long enough in the arm for the Amati now."'

Myra could scarcely get out the words.

'You didn't bring it with you?'

Mr Ruttenstein pointed to the top drawer of the wardrobe. 'It's in there.'

Myra got up and opened the drawer. Inside was a worn violin case. She lifted it out, laid it on the end of the bed and opened it. Inside was a violin made of such warm-coloured wood it looked soft to touch. In the lid were two bows with gold on them. Underneath was a little plate on which was written: 'For Sebastian Forum from his friend, P. G. Ruttenstein in gratitude.' She said:

'Downstairs in the hall is Sebastian's tutor – Paul.'

'Paul Ingle! I know him.'

'Paul will get that fiddle to Sebastian faster than anyone else.'

'Is he allowed to see anyone?'

'Things like that don't worry Paul.'

'Send Mr Ingle up,' Mr Ruttenstein said into the phone.

Sebastian had no idea of the attention he was causing nor of how many people came and went from round his bed. He was off on his lonely search. It seemed as if the world had grown misty and somewhere, centuries away, the Amati was calling. Then suddenly a voice fetched him back to the nursing home.

'Look, old son. Paul here. I've got a present for you. It's from friend Ruttenstein. It's the Amati.'

18

Journey's End

Although as soon as he had the Amati Sebastian began to get well he was slow about it. Meanwhile plans had to be made. It was like leaving Apple Bough all over again, for whenever David and Polly were in Number 10 they went into a room by themselves and talked and talked. Wolfgang, who was anyway feeling cross and loose-end-ish now his television play was over, was always muttering about them.

'Who would think that Myra was fourteen and me twelve? They yatter, yatter as if we were babies not able to understand plans.'

Ethel agreed with him for she was cross and loose-end-ish too, for she hated a holiday from dancing.

'I suppose it's about Sebastian and when he'll be well enough to play a concert, but he's had Daddy and Mummy since February, and we haven't had them at all. I would have hoped now he's better they would have time for us.'

Even Myra, who was not feeling loose-end-ish, felt it was

a bit mean to be so secret about plans. So one day she told Paul how she felt.

'We all know Sebastian can't play at concerts this autumn, and we all know when he's better we're going to Devonshire, so why secrets?'

Paul gave her a thoughtful look.

'Perhaps it's nothing to do with that.'

'Whatever it's to do with I should think Wolf and Ettie might go to Devonshire. They need a holiday.'

Paul gave her another funny look.

'That's not a bad idea. Why don't you suggest it?'

Visits to Sebastian, except from Polly and David, had to be rationed as he still got tired easily. But that afternoon Myra was to visit him so David and Polly took her with them to the nursing home in a taxi.

It was not as easy as Myra had expected to make her suggestion, for David and Polly kept talking and talking about other things, but at last she got a word in.

'I was wondering. Do you think Wolf and Ettie could go to Devonshire now? They've both been working hard and truthfully I think they need a holiday.'

David and Polly exchanged a queer look. Then David said:

'You've had a busy time too, it can't have been much fun hanging around the film and television studios.'

'Oh, no, please, not me,' Myra said hurriedly. 'I would much rather wait for Sebastian.'

Again David and Polly exchanged looks which Myra thought were queer.

'It might be an idea,' David said doubtfully, 'but someone

ought to go with them and Miss Popple wants to spend her holiday with her brother.'

'I thought Paul could go perhaps,' Myra suggested. 'I mean, Sebastian won't do lessons for ages, will he?'

Polly conceded that. Then she said:

'The more I think of it the more I like the idea. Don't you see, David, Wolfie, Ettie and Paul could go now. Then we could go later and when he's really fit Myra could bring Sebastian by car.'

They looked at each other as if they were seeing something Myra could not see. Then David nodded.

'It's a superb idea, far better than the original plan. I'll ring the parents tonight and tell them to expect them.'

Wolfgang and Ethel were charmed to travel with Paul, and Paul was delighted to be going to Devonshire.

'Now don't worry, Mrs F.,' he said before they left for the train, 'leave everything to me, I'll have even Wolf under control before you see him again.'

The house felt horribly empty when Wolfgang and Ethel had gone, and it felt worse two days later when Miss Popple left to stay with Dan. But Myra did not mind Miss Popple going so much as she would have done if she had not become as secretive as David and Polly before she left, always what Wolfgang called yattering to them behind closed doors.

'And there's nothing to have secrets about,' Myra told Wag. 'Sebastian's better and we all know we're going to Devonshire. Why must grown-ups be so peculiar?'

Then Sebastian became strange. He had not been strong enough for much more than being talked to at first. But now he was not only getting well again but, in some ways, looking more well than he had looked for ages, and when this began to happen he too had secrets. He would scruffle papers out of sight when Myra came to visit him, and he was cagey about what other people had said to him, and particularly he was cagey about what Mr Ruttenstein and he talked about.

Mr Ruttenstein had made a habit of coming in to see Sebastian for a few minutes at about five o'clock each evening. It was no secret that he came and Myra supposed he talked about music. Then one day – it was the first day Sebastian was sitting in a chair – Myra said:

'Do you like seeing Mr Ruttenstein every day – I mean it's so odd, before he just arranged your tours. Now he's like a friend.'

Sebastian looked at Myra and grinned.

'What about you? You had breakfast with him in his bedroom.'

Myra did not like to think of that dreadful morning when Sebastian was so ill, so she never talked about it.

'Did he tell you?'

'Of course.' Sebastian's eyes turned to the top of his cupboard where he could see the end of the violin case. 'I wish they'd let me play it, Myra, but I'm only allowed to hold it.'

'I expect you can play a bit in Devonshire.'

Sebastian again looked as if he might laugh.

'Mr Ruttenstein told me that after you sent Paul here with the Amati you had a proper breakfast.'

Myra nodded.

'I couldn't have been more surprised. He was awfully nice. We'd never thought he'd be that, did we?'

Sebastian fiddled with the blanket which covered his knees.

'What did you talk about?'

Myra saw herself again. Very smeared and tear-stained she must have looked, but she wasn't going to tell Sebastian that.

'Things. About how it was before you became famous. He'd never seen Apple Bough. He asked questions and asked questions. Then he asked about Number 10. I told him about Operation Home. He doesn't know the Marshalls so I didn't think it would matter telling him that I didn't like their furniture.'

Sebastian stared out of the window.

'He's nice really. He doesn't mind a bit I can't play at concerts until after Christmas.'

'Shall you go on playing? I mean, now you haven't got to earn the Amati?'

Sebastian turned round, surprised.

'Of course. I can't wait to give a concert playing it. But Mr Ruttenstein thinks I should travel less and spend longer Rest Periods here.'

Myra thought of Number 10.

'Perhaps if you're at Number 10 more it could have different furniture, even perhaps our own out of store. I don't think Number 10 will ever be a real proper home, but I suppose I'll get used to it.'

The doctor said that Sebastian could go home on the following Saturday. It was announced on a Monday and to Myra's surprise David and Polly left for Devonshire the next morning.

'There's such a lot to do,' Polly explained.

'Must have everything shipshape for the invalid,' David pointed out.

Myra, with Wag, waved them off then, feeling dismal, she went to the kitchen to find the Bottles.

'It feels very empty, doesn't it?'

'Come and 'ave a cuppa,' Mrs Bottle invited. 'It's only for a day or two, and you do see your Mum and Dad must go a'ead to see everything's nice for Sebastian.'

'But everything's always nice in Devonshire. Grandmother is a very scrubbing, cleaning sort of person.'

'I'm sure,' Mr Bottle agreed. 'But when you've been as queer as our Sebastian you want things special.'

Myra accepted the cup of tea and the piece of cake Mrs Bottle gave her, and she pretended she agreed with Mr Bottle, but inside she thought everyone was getting odder and odder.

Then the oddest thing of all happened. Mumsdad and Mumsmum came round on the Friday evening to say there was to be a new film for Wolfgang, so at first they talked about that.

'Wolfie will be crazy on it,' Mumsdad said. 'As far as I can make out he's the leader of a boys' orchestra, he's the conductor and is supposed to write his own music.'

Myra tried to be glad.

'How lovely for Wolf! Don't you think we better ring him up and tell him? He'll be thrilled.'

Mumsmum spoke so quickly it was almost as if she was cross.

'No!' Then she added, as if to explain: 'No – much better if you tell him when you see him tomorrow.'

That was when the oddest thing happened. Mumsdad took a letter from his pocket.

'Talking of tomorrow. Sebastian's car is to call for you at five o'clock.'

'Five! Isn't that awfully early?'

'At night,' said Mumsdad, as if it was the usual time to leave for Devonshire.

'Five at night!' Myra gasped.

Mumsmum spoke in a there's-nothing-unusual-about-it voice.

'The roads will be empty, so it will be less tiring for Sebastian.'

Myra could not believe it.

'Are you sure? We won't get there till awfully late.'

'I think you must leave it to the doctor to decide,' Mumsmum said firmly. 'And he's decided six o'clock from the nursing home.'

Saturday seemed one of the longest days Myra had ever known, for she had expected to be travelling in the morning and had not thought she would be there all day. Mumsmum and Mumsdad tried to help for they took her to lunch with them, but Myra was very glad when it was five o'clock.

The Bottles, behaving as if it was they who were going to Devonshire, helped the chauffeur pack the cases in the boot. Then Mrs Bottle gave Myra a hug.

'Goodbye, ducks. Be ever so happy, won't you? Goodbye, Wag.'

'But don't forget us,' Mr Bottle added.

Sebastian, looking much longer in the leg and very large

about the eyes, was waiting in the nursing-home hall. He was bursting with impatience to get off.

'I thought you were never coming,' he told Myra as they drove away.

'Nobody could have thought that more than me. I never knew so long a day. It's a pity it will be dark so we don't see the beginnings of Devonshire.'

It took so long to get out of London that it was dusk by the time they were in the country. Myra peered out of the window.

'It's real country now. I can see hedges with Old Man's Beard growing and there are hardly any lights.'

Sebastian did not answer, he seemed to have gone to sleep.

Driving in a car in the dark makes people sleepy, and presently Myra's head sagged forward.

She woke with a jump for the car was slowing up.

'We're here,' said Sebastian. He sounded excited. 'You and Wag get out.'

The chauffeur opened the door and Myra and Wag jumped out. Nobody seemed to be about, and it looked wrong for Devonshire. They were in a dark lane, and the white gate was not the gate of the rectory. Then suddenly Myra knew. Her voice rose to a shout.

'It's Apple Bough, Sebastian! It's Apple Bough!'

Sebastian was in bed and the rest of the family, except Ethel who was dancing round the room, sitting on it, before Myra learnt how everything had happened.

'It began with you telling Mr Ruttenstein about Apple Bough,' Sebastian explained.

'I must say,' Wolfgang admitted, 'that I've stopped abhorring Mr Ruttenstein.'

'It was he who made the people sell Apple Bough,' Sebastian went on.

'And it was he,' David put in, 'who thought Sebastian should buy Apple Bough as a present for you, Myra.'

'Me!' Myra was stunned. 'Apple Bough mine!'

Ethel stopped dancing to give Myra a hug.

'Your very own. But truthfully the rest of us don't want it, except as a place to come home to.'

Wolfgang tugged at Myra's arm.

'When we were in Devonshire it was Grandfather who thought of you getting here when it was dark. He said otherwise you'd see where you were going.'

'You can imagine the rush, darling,' said Polly. 'Even though we took over the carpets and curtains with Apple Bough there was so much to do; all the furniture to get out of store.'

Myra pinched herself.

'I can't believe it.'

'I'm going to stay here almost all the time until Christmas,' said Sebastian.

'So are Mummy and I,' David added, 'and anyway, Miss Popple will be here, and when we sell Number 10 and get a flat perhaps the Bottles.'

Myra found it difficult to take it all in.

'The Bottles! How utterly glorious!'

Wolfgang put on his showing-off voice.

'As I'm starring in this new picture I'll be a lot at the new flat; Daddy says Paul will look after me.'

'Discipline you is the word,' said David.

Wolfgang dismissed that.

'But I'll come down here for weekends when I can.'

Ethel turned a neat pirouette.

'I'll be a boarder at The Royal Ballet School but I'll be able to come here some weekends.'

Myra felt she might burst from too much happiness. She got up to look out of the window. The moon was out, the garden looked perfect. It had been tidied since she had last seen it. But it was still the best sort of garden.

'That's all right. Apple Bough will be waiting whenever you can come home – and, of course, so will I.'

If you enjoyed
Apple Bough,
we think you will also love

Caldicott Place

by Noel Streatfeild

Caldicott Place

When their father is injured in an accident, life changes for the Johnstone family. Unable to afford their home, they must move to a small London flat. There is no money for Carol's ballet lessons and Tim is heartbroken as he cannot take Jelly, his beloved dog, with him.

Then, in an extraordinary twist of fate, Tim inherits a country house, Caldicott Place, where the family – including Jelly – can live together. But the house is badly in need of repair and they have no money, so a solution is found – the family start to look after wealthy boarding-school children in the holidays. Although they dread the prospect of sharing their newly found home with spoiled rich children, friendships can be found in the unlikeliest places.

The Accident

'It is queer,' Bill once said, 'how you don't notice how nice things are while they are being nice; it's only when they stop being nice that you find out.'

Poor Bill, he had every reason to say this and so had Carol and Tim. For things had always been – allowing for the small set-backs which happen to everybody – so very, very nice until their father's accident.

The Johnstones lived in a new town in a pleasant house with a garden and a garage. Their father was a foreman of a factory in London and drove to and from work every day. He was the nicest sort of father, always interested in anything his family were doing and he did his best to help. His own hobby was his garden but he was anything but a mean gardener. Most keen gardeners of a not very big but showy little garden say a dog is death to it. The family had – or to be correct, Tim had – a queer little dog. Tim had found him when he was a puppy, lost, miserable and cold. Even though the puppy was small Tim, who was then only four, had found him heavy to carry and had literally staggered into the house and almost dropped the puppy in the doorway.

'Mum,' he had gasped. 'Mum. Look what I've found.'

'Poor little thing,' his mother had said. 'We must find out whom he belongs to.'

Tim had known she would say that.

'He's nothing on his collar. I looked.'

By now Bill, who was at that time ten, and Carol, who was seven, had joined them.

'I think he's a sort of poodle,' Bill had said. 'I mean he's got that sort of fur but straight.'

Carol had knelt down by the puppy.

'His nose isn't quite poodle-ish, more like that dachshund in the pet shop.'

'Whatever kind of dog he is,' their mother had said, 'we must ring the police to fetch him.'

Six reproachful eyes looked at her.

'You weren't thinking of taking him to a Police Station, were you?' Carol had asked in a very shocked voice.

Their mother had weakened.

'Not just now perhaps but I must let the police know I have him, his poor owner may be waiting for him.'

But no owner had been waiting for the little dog that day or any day, so he became a part of the family. He was named Jellicoe because it was by a block of flats called Jellicoe Buildings that Tim had found him, but he was never called Jellicoe – just Jelly.

'Are you sure you want the children to keep Jelly?' their mother had said to their father when it was obvious that no one was going to claim the puppy. 'He'll ruin your garden.'

Their father had laughed.

'I'll put fencing everywhere and if Jelly gets through it then I'll make the children replace it. As a matter of fact I'm rather glad Jelly's been forced on us. I should have found it hard to buy a dog, thinking of my flowers, but the children ought to have one, no family is complete without a dog.'

Their father who, before he was a foreman had made precision tools, was very neat with his fingers. Anything that his children wanted he was able to make. Angels' wings for the school nativity play. A head-dress like a rose when Carol danced in her dancing-class display. In fact so clever was he that over the years when something particularly difficult was wanted for a school or dancing-class entertainment the teachers would say to whichever child was involved, 'Do you think your father would help?'

Their father was a great party man. Weeks before Christmas he always worked out something new and startling in the way of Christmas decorations with which to thrill the family and visitors. He always thought out exciting things too for the family birthdays.

'You pretend you plan things for the children,' their mother would say, 'but really it's for yourself. The trouble is you've never grown up.'

Whatever the reason their father certainly was a wonderful planner. Bill's birthday was in August, a time when the family was away on holiday. Every year, wherever they went, their father had what the family called 'Bill's mystery drive' arranged. It was always to somewhere special with a superb picnic as part of it, and it was always the high spot of the holiday.

Carol's birthday was at the end of January and was kept on the Saturday following it. It was a lunch-out matinée occasion. But it was no 'where shall we eat?' day, every moment was worked out by their father, and thrilling places he found to eat in, almost always foreign with strange exotic foods. When the children were small their mother said she was scared to death in case one of them was sick in the theatre.

Tim's birthday was the fifth of November and that of course settled itself. Being Guy Fawkes day it had to be a bonfire-and-fireworks party, but what a bonfire and what fireworks! Locally all fireworks were judged by Tim's birthday ones. 'They were nearly up to the Tim Johnstone standard' or 'They weren't bad but nowhere near the Tim Johnstone style.'

It was in the August when Bill was going to be thirteen, Carol had been eleven last January, Tim would be eight in November and Jelly was believed to be four that the dreadful thing happened. It was the night before they went away for the summer holidays; they were going to Cornwall that year.

'I'm going to get the car filled up tonight,' their father called out. 'I don't want to waste time tomorrow because I want to get the back of the journey broken before lunch.'

Their mother was packing.

'All right, dear,' she answered, her mind on what she was doing.

'Can I go with Dad?' Tim asked.

'No,' said his mother. 'You don't move until you've laid out on your bed all the toys and things you want to take.'

It was one of those accidents which nobody saw. A

chauffeur-driven car with an old lady called Lady Paine in the back turned out of a drive and crashed into their father's car. The chauffeur was killed and Lady Paine and their father taken to hospital unconscious. Without doubt the chauffeur was to blame; it was he who shot out of a drive into Father's car. Lady Paine's insurance company would pay but not until it was known if Father was permanently damaged.

Their father was unconscious for nearly three weeks. Then slowly he regained consciousness but he came back not like his proper self. It was after he had been conscious for nearly two weeks that Bill went to see him; until then nobody but his mother had visited.

'Sister thinks you'd better see him, Bill,' his mother said. 'She says he's as well as can be expected but it may be months before he can work again – the doctors are moving him to a psychiatric hospital for treatment.' Her voice wobbled she was trying so hard not to cry. 'We must make some sort of plan.'

'Does Dad know how long he may be ill?' Bill asked.

'The doctors said he was to be told but I don't know if he quite understood. They want him to take an interest in things. But he just won't. Oh, Bill, I'm afraid you're in for a shock, he's so changed.'

Bill gave his mother's shoulder an awkward pat.

'Don't fuss. He'll be all right in the end.'

His mother choked back a sob.

'He can't remember what happened, which is natural. But he's so odd, he knows he's been in hospital for nearly five weeks and he knows we haven't got any insurance money yet, but he seems quite happy to lie there for ever. He's not a bit worried about what is to happen to us.'

'What do you mean – happen to us?' Bill asked.

His mother hesitated, not wanting to worry him more than she had to, then it was such a relief to have someone to talk to she just burst out with everything.

'The firm are being very good paying Dad as usual, but it can't go on for ever. Some day the old lady's insurance will pay up but that will take time. The doctors say that it may be months before he's back to normal.' She again hesitated. 'Sometimes I wake in the night scared that he will never be.'

Bill felt he was growing up every minute. His father had always been the planner and the arranger for them all, he had never asked him for advice – or anybody else if it came to that. He supposed really Dad had treated him as a child, which was of course ridiculous when you were almost thirteen. Now he was thirteen as he talked to his mother, he felt taller and sort of broader in the shoulders.

'I'll visit Dad instead of you tomorrow evening. He'll feel different talking to me – you know, not being grown-up and all that.'

Bill told Carol and Tim he was going to the hospital, but he didn't tell them anything that his mother had told him, for both of them had, of course, been upset by the accident, particularly Carol who, since it had happened, had cried about anything and was easily cross.

'I know we've all sent flowers and fruit and stuff, but now Dad's getting better can you think up something to send him he might like to do?'

'I could,' said Tim, 'but I'll save it up for when I visit him.'

'That's what I think I'll do,' Carol agreed. 'If you can go tomorrow perhaps Mum will take us the next visiting day.'

Bill thought, if his mother was only half right, neither Carol nor Tim should be allowed to see their father until he was miles better.

'I think there are rules about how many of us he can see. Anyway let me take something from you both tomorrow.'

'What sort of thing to do?' Carol asked. 'Do you mean like a jigsaw puzzle?'

Bill shook his head.

'No, the hospital will have those. You know the sort of thing he likes doing and the hospital doesn't. It needn't cost much but, of course, done up properly seeing what a parcel man he is.'

The next evening Bill, with rather a beating heart for he was shy of the big public ward with everyone, he felt, staring at him, turned up at his father's bedside.

His father was propped up in a sitting position and, except that there was a huge scar on his forehead and that he was very pale, he looked far more himself than his mother had led him to expect.

'Hullo, Dad, how're things?'

Very slowly his father turned his head to look at Bill and for a second it seemed as if he did not recognise him. Then he smiled.

'Hullo, old man.'

Bill put the parcels and an envelope on the bed; each parcel was wrapped in fancy paper.

'This is from Carol, this is from Tim, this is from me and the envelope is from Jelly.'

It was then Bill saw what was frightening his mother. If ever there was a parcel-minded man it had been his father, which was why they had done their parcels up in grand paper. Now his father didn't even give them a glance.

'How kind,' he said in a far-away voice and turned his head as if he didn't even want to look at the parcels.

Bill didn't know what to say or do next so he opened Carol's parcel. Carol usually had two and sixpence a week pocket money but it never had been enough so her father had usually helped out when anything special was wanted. Since the accident it had been just two and sixpence and it had to cover everything including subscriptions, which it never had been expected to cover before. There were therefore signs of poverty about Carol's present. It was packed in last birthday's paper. Inside was an exercise book with lined pages on one side with plain sheets facing it to draw on. On the top of the first page Carol had printed very neatly HOSPITAL DIARY OF FREDERICK JOHNSTONE. Bill thought it a wonderful present and it went well with his.

'I say, Dad, look at this.' His father held the book which Bill pressed into his hand but he didn't look, so Bill tore open his own present, which was coloured pencils.

'And these are just right for drawing in it. You can draw the other patients and the nurses and ... ' He stopped because really talking to his father was like talking into space. Miserably he undid Tim's parcel. Tim only had one shilling a week, it would rise to one and sixpence when he got into double figures. He never had any money saved but he had taken trouble over his present, which really Bill thought was better than spending money. He had been to the plant shop and persuaded the owner to give him a seed catalogue. He had no birthday paper but he had found an old piece of Christmas paper to wrap the catalogue in. Bill was full of admiration and sounded it.

'Look what Tim's sent you! While you're in bed is just the time to work out what seeds you want to plant. Look at some of these pictures, you know you like looking at catalogues.' His father wouldn't even take hold of the catalogue.

'Seeds,' he said vaguely. 'Please thank Tim.'

Bill hardly had the heart to open Jelly's envelope. He knew what was in it for he had bought it himself. It was a get-well card, the sort that usually his father would have thought very funny. It had a picture of a man all over bandages lying in bed, with a fearful-looking wife sitting beside him. Outside it said: 'Sorry about your accident.' Inside there was a verse about getting well.

'And Jelly sent this card,' Bill's voice faded away on 'this card' for it was clear his father wasn't listening.

Quite soon the effort of trying to talk without getting an answer was too much for Bill so he got up.

'Goodbye, Dad, I'll be in again soon.'

It was clear his father didn't care if he came again or not for he just said:

'Thanks, old man,' and shut his eyes.

At the door of the ward the Sister in charge stopped Bill. 'How did you find your father?'

Bill stared at her with frightened, unhappy eyes.

'Awful.'

Sister nodded.

'I know. But I'm sure he'll pick up when we can move

him to the other hospital. Do come again. He may be more interested than you think and anyway if you share the visiting it helps your mother.'

Outside the hospital Bill stood pulling himself together before he faced his mother. What was he to say to her? Suppose his father never got better what was going to happen to them?

DISCOVER
Virago Children's Classics

virago